Visual Studio
C# Programming
and PC interfacing

Dr John Allwork

British Library Cataloguing in Publication Data
A catalogue record for this book is available from the British Library

ISBN 978-0-905705-95-8

Prepress production: Kontinu, Sittard
Cover design: Frederik Helfrich, Deventer
First published in the United Kingdom 2010
Printed in the Netherlands by Wilco, Amersfoort, second print April 2013
© Elektor International Media BV 2010

109027-UK

Contents

About the Author

John Allwork was born in 1950 in Kent, England and became interested in electronics and engineering at school. He went to Sheffield University on their BEng Electrical and Electronic Engineering course. There he developed an interest in computers and continued his education on an MSc course in Digital Electronics and Communication at UMIST. After two years working for ICL as design, commissioning and test Engineer he returned to UMIST where he graduated with a PhD in 'Design and Development of Microprocessor systems'

He worked for several years in technical support and as a manager in electronics distribution, working closely with Intel Application Engineers and followed this with design work on the Inmos Transputer systems.

He has been a lecturer at Manchester Metropolitan University in the Department of Engineering and Technology since 1991.

His interests apart from electronics include skiing, walking and spending time on his allotment or on his narrowboat.

Introduction

This book is aimed at anyone who wants to learn about C# programming and interfacing to a PC. It covers programming concepts from the basics to object oriented programming, displaying graphs, threading and databases. The PC interfacing chapters cover internet communications, using a sound card for analogue input and output, and using the USB port to control external hardware.

Although it assumes a little knowledge of programming it actually starts from the basics and covers the Visual Studio development environment, the .NET framework and C# programming language from data types and program flow to more advanced concepts such as object oriented programming. It continues with program debugging, file handling, databases, threading, internet communication using TCP/IP and UDP and graphs and plotting before moving to hardware interfacing using serial and parallel ports and the USB port. It includes three new chapters on DirectX drivers, interfacing to PIC processors and using the USB port.

It is complete with many program examples, self assessment exercises and links to supporting videos. Full program examples are available, as is support for University lecturers in the form of PowerPoint presentations for most chapters.

The original book has been updated for Visual Studio 2010 and more relevant videos have been sourced or produced to accompany the book. It has been checked using the Windows 7 operating system.

I do not pretend to know all there is about C# and the .NET framework. I have a background in hardware design and writing software to control it. There may be mistakes in the book at which programmers may be offended and I am sure there are better ways to write some of the code, but I have written and tried all the examples and know they work. I hope the examples will spur you on to find solutions to your own problems. Should you need more information then please try the on-line help and the Microsoft forums. There are plenty of programmers out there willing to help solve your problems, often extremely quickly.

I wish to thank my friends and colleagues for encouraging me and checking the manuscript, especially Paul Ridgway, Dr Hugh Frost, Dr George South and Dr Nader Anani; my students who have unwittingly helped me clarify and enhance the book; Matt Howlett from NPlot for permission to use their images; Don Powrie from DLP Design, Inc. for help and clarification of the USB module protocol and hardware interfacing; and the many anonymous people on the internet, forums, blogs and websites who have answered many questions, not just my own – keep up the good work. Not least of all I would like to thank my wife for supporting me throughout.

And of course you for buying the book!

Conventions used in this book

A few conventions used in the book, used mainly to distinguish normal text from C# code and program output.

Normal text	Times New Roman - Used for plain text
Program code	Arial - C# source code and snippets of code
Program output	Courier New – program output in MSDOS window

I have also used the 'greater than' symbol to indicate that the reader should follow a sequence of commands, such as File > New Project > Windows application.

Chapter 1 - The Visual Studio 2010 C# Environment

1.1 Introduction

C# is a modern programming language and the Visual Studio environment lets you write graphical user based programs for Windows. The .NET framework provides extensive interface libraries. Programs written in C# can be used alongside programs written in VB.NET and F# and J# code. The programs are compiled to an intermediate language, or common language runtime CLR, which is then run on the specific computer, see figure 1.1. This makes your C# programs platform independent. Of course we will be dealing solely with writing programs for the PC.

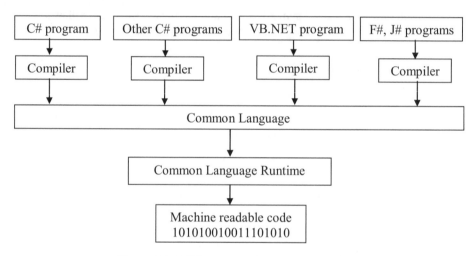

Figure 1.1 .NET common language operation

This design means that C# programs run slower than truly compiled programs such as C++, but the benefits outweigh the disadvantages. C# is known as managed code. This means that security, access and memory allocation and storage are controlled by the CLR. The .NET framework also provides access to programs that execute outside the framework, in our case access to hardware ports using the P/Invoke feature. The current version of the .NET framework (version 4) was released in April 2010 with Visual Studio 2010.

1.1.1 What's new in VS2010?

To be honest, most of what's new is beyond the scope of this book, but there are a few enhancements to the IDE including highlighting references, a quicker way to find all references and a new zoom feature. The Professional edition has a new 'Team Explorer' window, an aid for software development. For more information please refer to 'What's new in Visual C# 2010' at:

http://msdn.microsoft.com/en-us/library/bb383815.aspx.

You can also look at the codeproject's review at:
http://www.codeproject.com/KB/aspnet/Whatis_New_ASP_Net_4.aspx

1.2 Obtaining the Visual C# 2010 software

Visual C# 2010 is part of the Visual Studio suite of software and the Express Edition can be downloaded for free from the Microsoft web site. The Express Edition is ideal for learning the language and contains nearly everything we shall need. The software is available at

http://www.microsoft.com/express/Downloads/

Choose your language and select 'Free Download'. You may have to un-install any previous versions of the software. If you want to use databases also install SQL Server 2008 Express; only the SQL Server Database Engine is needed. The whole process takes a few minutes.

You are reminded to register, but it's a good idea and an easy process. You can do this from the Help > Register Product menu within Visual Studio.

The Microsoft forums are a good place to go for help and if you get stuck there's help at: http://forums.microsoft.com/msdn:

MSDN Forums>Visual Studio Express Editions>Installing and registering.

There are plenty of videos available from Microsoft which are mentioned later.

At this stage it may be a good idea to check you have the latest version of the .NET framework.

It is also possible to download a version of the Professional edition, but this has a 90-day limit.

1.3 The Visual Studio development environment

The development environment enables you to create, run and debug your program via a graphical user interface (GUI). When you run Visual Studio it starts with an introductory page, see figure 1.2. If you are really new to the environment, have a look at the 'What's New in Visual C# 2010 Express box.

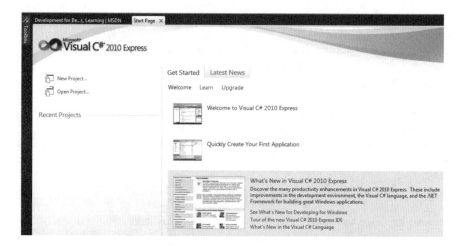

Figure 1.2 Visual Studio introductory page

To start a new C# project, click the New Project option or choose File > New Project from the main menu. You can then choose from a selection of options. We shall be using 'Windows Forms Application', but note that you can create a Console Application or a WPF (Windows Presentation Foundation) Application, see figure 1.3.

Figure 1.3 C# project applications

Type a name for your project in the Name box, e.g. 'HelloWorld' and click OK to display the development environment, see figure 1.4. They won't all be there initially and some of the windows may be minimized, we'll see how to display the windows soon.

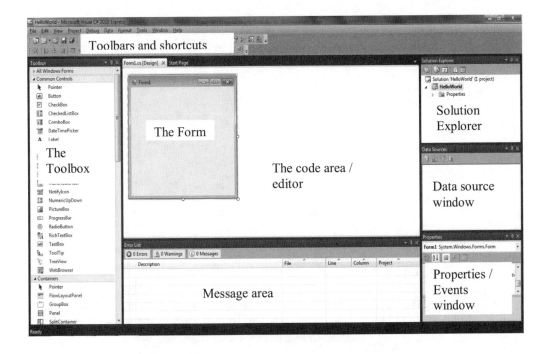

Figure 1.4 The C# development environment.

In the centre is the form where we will create our design by placing controls such as buttons, labels and text boxes, etc. Behind this is the editing area for our code. The Toolbox is on the left. The short-cut icons at the top; the Solution Explorer, Data Sources and Properties Windows are on the right and the error window at the bottom. The toolbox expands to show the controls when you click it. To display it permanently click the icon that looks like a drawing pin. If the toolbox or any of the other windows aren't displayed, select View> Toolbox (Properties Window, Task list etc.). The tabs above the form will display our code and other development windows. You can drag the windows around to create your own preferred layout.

Users who are familiar with VS2008 and earlier versions will notice the new layout toolbar at the top of the screen.

1.3.1 The Form

This is the most important part of the GUI design, see figure 1.5. In development it is where the controls (buttons, labels, text boxes etc.) are placed. When the program runs, it is what the user finally sees and how they interact with your program.

Figure 1.5 The form.

We shall see how we can change the title and the icon later.

1.3.2 The Code Editor.

Double clicking the form or a control placed on the form will display the code editor. A new tab appears called Form1.cs and this is where you will type your code, see figure 1.6.

```
Form1.cs*  ×  Form1.cs [Design]*
HelloWorld.Form1                                        Form1_Load(obj
namespace HelloWorld
{
    public partial class Form1 : Form
    {
        public Form1()
        {
            InitializeComponent();
        }

        private void Form1_Load(object sender, EventArgs e)
        {
            |
        }
    }
}
```

Figure1.6 The code editor

Notice that some code is already inserted for you, but you will still have to write the important parts!

Warning: Do not delete code that you have not typed as this will cause an error when you compile your code.

To return to the design, click the Form1.cs[Design] tab.

1.3.3 The Toolbox.

The toolbox contains the controls we will use in our user interface, see figure 1.7.

Figure 1.7 The Toolbox

You can choose to hide the toolbox or display it permanently. If it is hidden, to display it just move the cursor over the Toolbox icon. Click the drawing pin icon to permanently show or hide the toolbox. In order to place a control on the form, simply click the control and drag it to the form.

The tools are grouped in similar functions; Common controls (buttons, labels, text boxes), Containers (tabbed forms, panels), Menus & Toolbars, etc. We shall introduce the controls as we need them. Note that you can only select controls from the toolbox when the design tab is selected.

1.3.4 The properties and events box

All controls have their own properties. For example a button will have a certain position on the form (properties: Top and Left), a size (Height and Width), Text and Font etc. They are all listed in the properties box. Figure 1.8 shows the Text property of a TextBox highlighted.

Figure 1.8 TextBox properties

The order of the properties can be changed between alphabetical and categorized by clicking the first two icons in the properties box.
Clicking the lightning bolt icon will change the display to show the events for that control, e.g. Click, MouseHover or Move. Figure 1.9 shows the event icon selected and

the Click event for the button selected. A short description of the event is displayed at the bottom of the properties window.

Figure 1.9 Control click event display

Clicking the list icon to the left of the event icon will redisplay the properties list.

C# programs are event driven and these can be generated by the user, your program or the operating system. The program responds to these events. Different controls have different events, for example an event can be generated when text is typed into a textbox but that can't happen with a button. We will look at events later, but common events are:

- Clicking a button (Click event),
- Typing a key on the keyboard (KeyDown and KeyUp or combined to make a KeyPress)
- Mouse events (MouseMove, MouseDown, MouseUp, MouseMove, MouseClick)
- Drag events (DragDrop, DragEnter, DragLeave, DragOver)

Event driven programs can be difficult to debug and we shall see how to debug our programs later.

As you write your programs, the editor's 'IntelliSense' will prompt you for possible entries. The dot notation is used to access the methods, properties and events, e.g. button.Height. We shall cover methods and events later. Figure 1.10 shows some of the entries that can follow the full stop after 'button1.' has been typed.

Figure 1.10 IntelliSense prompt

To help you, different icons are used for a method (DrawToBitmap), a property (Enabled) and an event (EnabledChange), see figure 1.11.

Figure 1.11 Method, Property and Event icons

As you can see the IntelliSense editor also underlines code that it doesn't understand and will not prompt you further.

1.4 Exercises
1.4.1 Your First C# Program

To introduce you to the simplest and most common controls, let's write a Windows program to display 'Hello World' on the screen when a button is clicked. (The 'Hello World' is a common program used to introduce users to a new programming language)

1. Run Visual Studio C#, start a new Project (File>New Project), select Windows Application and rename it 'Hello world'. Choose the folder where you want you program to be saved.
2. Before continuing, save the project. Select File>Save All. Each project is saved in its own folder.
3. Display the form (click the Form1.cs[Design] tab). Select a button control from the Toolbox>Common Controls (use View > Toolbox if it's not displayed) and place it on the form (either click and drag the control, or click the control and then click the form), see figure 1.12.

Figure 1.12 Button control.

This will place a button named 'button1' on the form. Use the sizing handles to make it a sensible size.

4. Let's change the text displayed on the button. Display the properties window if necessary (View> Properties Window), scroll to the Text property and type in 'Hello world', see figure 1.13. Select the properties list icon if necessary to display the properties'

Figure 1.13 The Properties window

5. Text boxes are used to enter and display data'. This is where we will display the message 'Hello world' when our button is clicked. Select a TextBox control from the Toolbox and place it on the form. As you move it around the form alignment lines appear so you can align the controls. Place the controls side by side. Notice that the height of the text box is determined by its Font property, not by a Height property. The text property is currently blank.

6. Finally add one further control, a label. Click the label control and place it on the form above the others, and change its caption property to 'My First C# Program'.

Note how the size of the label automatically changes to fit the text. You may not want this and of course this is a property that can be changed.

7. Your form should be similar to figure 1.14.

Figure 1.14 Hello world GUI

Hint: You can delete any control by clicking it to select the control and pressing the 'delete' key.

8. Familiarise yourself with moving controls around the form. Click and hold the mouse button and move the mouse to move controls around, or single click to select the controls and use the re-sizing controls; the squares around the object, they are displayed on the button in figure 1.14.

9. If you want to try the layout toolbar, select both the button and text box by clicking and dragging around them. You can then align the controls to the left, centre, right, top, middle or bottom, change their size or spacing, see figure 1.15.

Figure 1.15 The layout toolbar

10. At this stage it is possible to run the program. Before running it, save the program. Click File>Save All. This will ask for a location, see figure 1.16. Note that all the project files will be saved in this folder and if you want to move your work to another PC, just copy the whole folder.

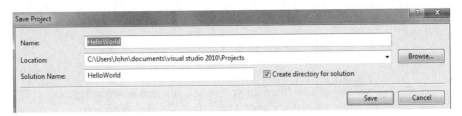

Figure 1.16 Saving the project

To run the program, click Debug>Start debugging, press the F5 function key or click the green triangle ('play' icon). There are often different ways to do the same operation and you will find your own preferred shortcuts.

Your 'program' will be compiled and run. You can't do much yet. You can click the button and enter text in the text box, even though you haven't written any code yet.

Stopping your program

You can close your program in the usual way by clicking the close button on Form1, see figure 1.17.

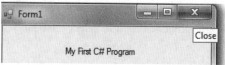

Figure 1.17 Stopping your program

Alternatively you can choose Debug > Stop Debugging or press shift-F5.

11. The button click event

The most used event is the button click. To write the code to display a message when the button is clicked, double-click the 'Hello world' button. Framework event code is added by the editor and you enter the code you want to execute between the curly brackets { }.

Between the curly brackets that have been added, type the following code:

```
textBox1.Text="Hello world";
```

This line of code changes the text in the textbox to 'Hello world' when the button is clicked. Note that C# is case sensitive and as we have seen the editor provides hints and code completion as you type. It also highlights in different colours code meanings such as keywords and strings.

The complete code for the button click is:

```
private void button1_Click(object sender, EventArgs e)
{
    textBox1.Text = "Hello world";
}
```

Remember some of this has been written for you. You only need to enter the code between the curly brackets. Also, if you didn't type the code, don't delete it.

12. Save the project and run it (press F5). When the button is clicked, it should display 'Hello world' in the text box.

Congratulations, you have just written and executed your first C# program!

The code is shown in figure 1.18. Remember you have only typed one line of this. We'll explain the other lines of code when we need them.

```
using System;
using System.Collections.Generic;
using System.ComponentModel;
using System.Data;
using System.Drawing;
using System.Linq;
using System.Text;
using System.Windows.Forms;

namespace HelloWorld
{
    public partial class Form1 : Form
    {
        public Form1()
        {
            InitializeComponent();
        }

        private void button1_Click(object sender, EventArgs e)
        {
            textBox1.Text = "Hello world";
        }
    }
}
```

Figure 1.18 The 'Hello World' code.

Save and close your application. Reload it and run it again. You can run the program by finding the HelloWorld.exe application file in the folder containing your files. It will be in the HelloWorld > bin > Debug folder

1.4.2 Copying files

The best way to transfer files between computers is to copy the whole folder and its files. For instance your program may reside in the folder:
"C:\Users\John\Documents\Visual Studio 2010\Projects\HelloWorld"

The HelloWorld folder contains the Visual Studio solution file and a second HelloWorld folder. The solution file can be clicked to open Visual Studio and your program. The HelloWorld folder contains the executable in the Debug folder, figure 1.19. You can create a release version when you are happy with your code.

Figure 1.19 Folders and files

To copy the program to another computer, just copy the top-level HelloWorld folder.

1.4.3 Common errors

I can't display the form.

If you can't find the tab, Try View > Designer, click Shift > F7 or click the icon in the Solution window, figure 1.20.

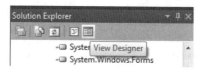

Figure 1.20 View Designer

The code can be viewed in the same way.

I get an error

Read the error message. You may not understand it, but clicking the message will take you to the line in error. Have you typed everything correctly? Did you delete something you hadn't typed in?

At this stage, it's most probably best to start again. Later, let's hope that later on we can understand the error messages!

How do I stop my program?

Use Debug > Stop Debugging, or press shift+F5.

It says parts of my program are missing.

Did you copy it from another PC? Did you copy all the files in the folder? Did you save the project and the .CS file before closing it last time? Have a look at section 1.4.2.

1.4.4 Properties exercises

Now that you understand how to change the control's properties, try changing them from within your program on the button click event:

1. Change the label's text, try: label1.Text = "new caption";

You can let the editor prompt you for the available properties. The text is a string and goes within double quotes. The semicolon is needed at the end of the statement.

2. Change the position of the button, label or textbox using 'Left' and 'Top' properties, say add 5 to each when the button is clicked and see how the textbox moves, e.g.

      button1.Left = button1.Left + 5;

3. Change the Width and colour of the textBox (using System.Drawing.Color.Red), the button's caption, or other properties, e.g.

      textBox1.Width = textBox1.Width + 45;
      textBox1.BackColor = System.Drawing.Color.Red;

Can you change the height of the textBox?

4. More button properties:
The Font property is used to change button's text. You can change the font, style, size, colour and effects. The BackColor and ForeColor properties change the colours and you can choose from System (Windows), Web or Custom colours. You can also choose an image to display on your button and hence could have any design on your button.

5. Exit program
You can add a button to close your program. There are two ways to do this in code. You can just exit from the application, or you can close the form. If your application has more than one form it will exit when you close the main form.

Add two buttons to your form and change their Name property to 'btnClose' and 'btnExit'. This will give you some idea what they are and do. This is more helpful than being called button1 and button2. We shall look at naming conventions later.

Add the following code for them respectively:

      this.Close( ) ;
                        and
      Application.Exit( );

We shall explain what is meant by 'this' later, but here it means the form itself.

Now you can close your program by clicking a button.

1.5 The Solution Explorer

Your code and Graphical User Interface (GUI) form design are combined into a project. The Solution Explorer shows how these are combined. In our first program we only have one form and its code, but there could be multiple forms.

My Solution Explorer looks like figure 1.21:

Figure 1.21 Solution Explorer

Hint: If the development environment isn't displaying what you need, try clicking within the Solution Explorer or clicking its icons.

1.6 Program execution.

If you look in your folder, you will see that the program application EXE file size is about 10kb. This is not the whole program. Your program will only run on another computer if it has the .NET framework installed. As we have mentioned, the C# compiler only compiles to intermediate code, which then runs under the .NET framework. This means it does run slower than truly compiled languages, but has the advantage that programs from different languages can be combined.

1.7 Number conversion.

The text in a Text box is held as a 'string' data type. If you want to deal with numbers, you have to convert from a number to a string and vice versa. We will see this in more detail later, but if you want to try it now, to convert to a string to display a number we use .ToString( ). Typical examples are:

```
// this is a comment - declare and initialise an integer number
int integerNumber = 42;
```

```
// convert the integer to string and display
textBox1.Text = integerNumber.ToString( ) ;

// declare and initialise a real number
double realNumber = 3.14159;

// convert the real number to a string and display
textBox1.Text = realNumber.ToString( ) ;
```

The above code declares an integer and a floating point number and converts them both to strings and displays them in a text box. The double-slash is a comment line.

We may need to convert numbers which have been typed into a textBox (i.e. a string) to an integer or floating point number. The Parse command is used to do this, for example Int32.Parse( ) or float.Parse( ), as follows:

```
// read a string and convert it to an integer
// declare an integer, i
int i;
// read textBox, convert to integer
i = Int32.Parse(textBox1.Text);
// square number and write back
textBox1.Text = (i * i).ToString( );

// read a string and convert it to a floating point number
// declare a realNumber
double realNumber;
// read text box and convert to floating point number
realNumber = float.Parse(textBox1.Text);
// square number and write back
textBox1.Text = (i * i).ToString();
```

Obviously if you try converting a string containing letters or a floating point number you will get an error. We shall see how we deal with errors later.

Try adding the first part of the code above (the integer code) to a button click event. It should read a number typed into the text box. Repeat for the real number code. Note that you will get a run-time error if the text box is empty or format is wrong, when the button is clicked.

You can also use Convert.ToInt32 which checks for a null value and returns a value of 0 if it is.

1.8 Exercise: Simple calculator

We shall demonstrate the number and string conversions using a simple calculator. It will have two text boxes for the numbers and one for the result. We shall provide the basic mathematical functions.

Start a new application (remember use File>New Project > Windows application, give it a suitable name).
Place three text boxes on the form, one for each of the two numbers to be calculated and one for the result. In this example we will use the default names for the controls.

Add four buttons, change the Text on each to '+', '-', '*', and '/'. Change the font size so the text looks good. Finally add an 'equals' label.

Your form should look like the example in figure 1.21.

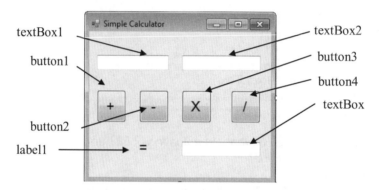

Figure 1.21 Calculator GUI design

The diagram has been labelled so you know which control is which. Later on we will discuss naming conventions and suggest sensible names so the control's function is obvious. We touched on this earlier, but you might like to think about suitable names for the controls now and use them.

Double-click the 'add' button and change the code for the button click event to the following:

```
private void button1_Click(object sender, EventArgs e)
{
    textBox3.Text = (double.Parse(textBox1.Text) +
                    double.Parse(textBox2.Text)).ToString( );
}
```

Here the calculation is all in one line of code so we don't have to declare any variables. The text box values are read and converted to floating point double precision numbers, added together, converted back to a string and placed in textBox3.

Save your project and run the program. Enter some numbers in the text boxes and see if it adds the numbers correctly.

We can declare and use variables if we want to. We will look at declaring variables in detail later, but you can try the following code for the subtract button:

```
private void button2_Click(object sender, EventArgs e)
{
    double fpNumber1, fpNumber2;
    fpNumber1 = double.Parse(textBox1.Text);
    fpNumber2 = double.Parse(textBox2.Text);
    textBox3.Text = (fpNumber1 - fpNumber2).ToString( );
}
```

Two double precision variables called fpNumber1 and fpNumber2 have been declared here and the values in the text boxes converted and placed in them.

See if you can add the code for the mutiply and divide buttons. The operators to use are: * and /.

If a text box is empty or doesn't hold a number a run-time error occurs. We shall see how to deal with this and use controls the ensure the user only enters correct values later.

1.9 Self Assessment Exercises

Video support.

1) Microsoft has a supporting installation and introductory video for VS2008 at:
   http://msdn.microsoft.com/en-us/beginner/bb964631.aspx

Although this covers installation and many features of Visual C# 2008 they are similar to those of VS2010. It also covers debugging and database access, so you might want to stop at 'Errors and Debugging' (after about 23 minutes) and return to it later.

2) Watch the MS videos 'What's new in Visual C# 2010 at:
   http://msdn.microsoft.com/library/a72418yk(VS.100).aspx

3) Watch the Tier Two Beginner Series videos at:
   http://msdn.microsoft.com/en-gb/beginner/bb308734.aspx

4) Watch the supporting videos pointed to at Elektor's web site

5) If you haven't done so, expand the Calculator program for the multiply and divide buttons yourself and check your calculator works. We will look at Mathematics functions later.

6) Take a look at the various ways of getting help.

   o   Select a control and press the F1 function key
   o   Click Help > Search and type in a search item
   o   Click Help > How do I? and look at the options
   o   Visit the Microsoft Developer Network Library at:
          http://msdn2.microsoft.com/en-us/library/default.aspx

1.10 Summary

This chapter has introduced the .NET framework, Visual Studio development environment and C# GUI design interface. The .NET framework provides libraries that we will use from our C# program.

The development environment windows have been seen: the form where the user interface design is created, the code window, the solution explorer, the properties and events windows and the toolbox. We have used common controls such as buttons, labels and the textbox. Some of the properties and events of these common controls have been used.

We have written a simple program to display a message. We have seen how numbers are converted to strings and we have written a basic calculator program.

Chapter 2 - Common controls, properties and events

2.1 Introduction

In the first chapter we saw the most commonly used controls; the button and textbox and some of their events. In this chapter we shall look at these controls in more detail and then look at more of the other common controls and their properties and events.

2.2 The Button

ab Button

The button's main properties are its appearance – Color, Image and Text; its behaviour – Enabled or Visible and its design - Name, Location and Size. Note the American spelling is used and remember our programs are case sensitive and the properties begin with a capital letter.

A useful property is the Tag property. This is free for you to use and can contain any type of information. All controls have a Tag property but if you want to use it you need to set the data type you want before you use it. We shall see how to use this later.

The button's main event is (button) Click, but it has Mouse events such as MouseEnter, MouseHover, MouseMove and MouseLeave. It also has events such as DragDrop and DragEnter to allow dragging and dropping of items, and surprisingly it also has keyboard events such as KeyDown and KeyPress.

2.3 The TextBox

abl TextBox

Looking at the TextBox will give us a chance to see how we deal with text generally.

The main properties are similar to the button (appearance, behaviour and design), but it also has text control properties.

Remember the Text property contains all the text in the TextBox. A textbox can have single or multiple lines which is set by the MultiLine property. The text can be ReadOnly and there are also other properties including WordWrap and AutoComplete.

These can all be seen in the properties box, see figure 2.1.

Figure 2.1 TextBox properties

The Textbox has the mouse and drag events mentioned for the button, but the keyboard events are more relevant for this control. They are TextChanged, KeyDown, KeyUp and KeyPress (a KeyDown followed by KeyUp). The events will occur when text is changed, or a key is pressed,

The individual keys can be read as they are typed by using the Keys codes (e.g. Keys.Enter), see the Self Assessment exercises for more details.

2.3.1 Dealing with text in a TextBox

The individual lines of text are held in the Lines property. To see this and add some text, place a textbox on the form and scroll to the Lines property in the Properties window, see figure 2.2. Remember, if this window isn't displayed, use View > Property Window to display it.

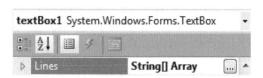

Figure 2.2 The TextBox lines property

It's a String array (a collection of words), but you don't have to understand what this means yet; we shall cover arrays later on.

Click the box with the three dots to display a dialog box where the text required in each of the lines of the textbox can be added, see figure 2.3.

Figure 2.3 Entering text into a TextBox

The Text property will contain all the text entered. It will be similar to figure 2.4.

Figure 2.4 TextBox Text property with multiple lines of text

When the program runs, the text is displayed all on one line as shown in figure 2.5.

Figure 2.5 TextBox with single line text

The default is for a single line of text. If you want multiple lines of text, set the MultiLine property true and expand the size of the textbox. The text will appear on individual lines as shown in figure 2.6.

Figure 2.6 TextBox with multiple lines of text

If the number of lines becomes too big for the textbox, horizontal and vertical scrollbars can also be displayed by selecting from the properties.

All the lines of text can be read in one go using the Text property (textBox1.Text). Individual lines can be read using the Lines[ ] property as follows:

    textBox1.Lines[0]

Note that Lines[0] is the first line.

To add lines to the TextBox, 'AppendText' is used. This is called a method. Controls like buttons and textboxes are objects and have Properties, Events and Methods. We have seen properties and events; a method is code that we call to do some work for us. In this case add text into the textbox. We shall more of this later and also write our own. To add text use the code:

```
textBox1.AppendText("new text");
```

This just appends text onto the last line and does not create a new line. To add text on to a new line, add the escape characters \r\n (meaning return and new line) as follows:

```
textBox1.AppendText("\r\nnew last line");
```

The total number of lines in the TextBox can be found with the Length property:

```
textBox1.Lines.Length;
```

So you can always access the last line with the code:

```
textBox1.Lines[textBox1.Lines.Length-1];
```

Remember, data in a textbox is held as a string and you may have to convert it to a form you need.

2.4 The ListBox control

ListBox

The List Box control contains a scrollable list of items that can be selected but not altered by the user (i.e. only changed from within the program).

Items are added at design time using Items > Collection in the same way as we did with the TextBox. Items can also can be added and removed by your program.

If you want to allow your user to select more than one item choose MultiSimple, or MultiExtended from the SelectionMode property. The first allows multiple selections but the second also allows use of control and shift to select multiple items.

As with the text box, individual lines are addressed using listBox.Items[x], where Items[0] is the first line. List box items are added using the code:

```
listBox1.Items.Add("string");
```

String conversion is done automatically, so you can add strings, integers, floating point numbers etc. You can have:

```
listBox1.Items.Add(34);            // add a number 34
listBox1.Items.Add("234");         // add text - 234
double f = 3.1415;
listBox1.Items.Add(f);             // add a floating point
```

You can try this now. Place a ListBox on your form and add the above code to a button click code. Run the program and confirm that the items are added to the List Box every time the button is clicked.

You can insert items at a specific position using the Insert method:

listBox1.Items.Insert (lineNo, "insertMe");

Individual items can be removed using the Remove method:

listBox1.Remove("string");   // remove the first occurrence of "string"

Or you can remove items at a specific line number using the RemoveAt method:

listBox1.RemoveAt(lineNo);

You can also clear the list box:

listBox1.Clear();

As you can see the ListBox has many commands. These are known as methods.

Eventually the item added is at the bottom of the list box and scroll bars appear. However the item just added isn't displayed – the user has to scroll to see it. If you want to display the last item added you can use the following code:

listBox1.SelectedIndex = listBox1.Items.Count-1;

If you want the scroll bars to be permanent, set the ScrollBarsAlwaysVisible property to true.

And finally to identify the selected item use the SelectedItem property:

listBox1.SelectedItem

2.5 The CheckedListBox

 CheckedListBox

The Checked List Box performs a similar operation to the list box, but with a check box beside each item.

The default event for both the list box and checked list box is SelectedIndexChanged which occurs when the user selects an item.

2.6 The CheckBox

 CheckBox

The CheckBox is used to select one or many items from a selection. The main property is of course if it is checked or not. It can be set or reset in code using the following:

```
CheckBox1.Checked = True;
CheckBox1.Checked = False;
```

Its main event occurs when its state is changed, CheckedChanged.

You may need to group checkboxes together. To do this place them within a contatiner such as a Panel, GroupBox or TabControl

2.7 The RadioButton

◉ RadioButton

RadioButtons are used when only one item from a list needs to be (or can only be) selected, e.g. first year, second year or third year. Selecting one will automatically switch the others off.

Should you need to have more than one group, for instance to select a student's course as well as their year, you need to put the radio buttons in separate containers such as a Panel or a GroupBox. We'll look at containers later.

The text beside a radio button is set by its text property and it has a checked property (true or false) which can be set or tested by the program.

Double-clicking the radio button will take you to the CheckedChanged event. You can check the radio button's checked state using the code:

```
if (radioButton1.Checked)
{
        // do something
}
```

2.8 The NumericUpDown control

NumericUpDown

If you want a user to enter a number you can use a text box, but then you will have to check the user enter a properly formatted number and request correct input if the input is wrong. The NumericUpDown control ensures your user can only enter numbers within a certain range. It displays a number with up and down buttons to change the number. The user can also enter in the required number in the box. If it is out of range the control will limit the number.

The minimum and maximum values the control will display are set by the Minimum and Maximum properties, and the current value is in the Value property. These can be set at design time or changed from within the program.

The default event for the NumericUpDown is ValueChanged. This event is triggered every time the value is incremented or decremented (which may not be what you want).

2.9 Displaying Images - the PictureBox control

The PictureBox control is used to display an image. To choose the picture for the image, select the image property, click the three dots (...) and browse for the image you want displayed. You can choose from a wide range of file formats including gif, jpg, bmp, or png. You can also display animated gifs.

The PictureBox tasks can be displayed by clicking the arrow icon at the top right hand corner of the picture, see figure 2.7. The picture can be shown in Normal, StretchImage, AutoSize, CenterImage and Zoom modes.

Figure 2.7 PictureBox Tasks.

If you want to select the picture to be displayed from a file, set the Image property using the Image.FromFile() method as follows:

```
pictureBox1.Image = Image.FromFile("filename");
```

The filename could be selected using an OpenFileDialog, which we will see later.

2.10 Focus and TabIndex

This is good place to mention focus. When a user clicks on a control it becomes the active control and is said to 'gain focus'. An Enter event also occurs. When a user clicks away from a control, it loses focus and a Leave event occurs. Of course don't have to write any code for these events if you don't want to. The order in which the controls gain focus when the user uses the tab key to move around the form's items is controlled by the TabIndex property. This is important if you want to guide your users around your interface sensibly and can make the difference between a usable or unusable interface!

2.11 Even more controls.

Some other controls you might like to look at are listed here. We will encounter some of these later. You will have used most of these in your windows applications, they are:

- Combo Box – a drop down list of selectable items
- DateTimePicker – to select a date and time
- MonthCalendar - to select a month
- ProgressBar – to indicate an operation's progress
- WebBrowser
- Print controls

2.12 The Containers controls toolbox

You might want to group items together on a form and the Containers controls are used to do that. The most common ones (apart from the form) are the Panel and the GroupBox. The Panel is a simplified version of the Group Box (it doesn't have border or a caption for instance). Containers can hold other containers. The container controls panel is shown in figure 2.8:

Figure 2.8. The Containers ToolBox

To see this working, place a Group Box on the form, then select a Checkbox and drag it over the Group Box. Now try moving the Group Box and notice that the Checkbox moves with it. We will use various containers in the design exercise in the next section.

Note however that a Form is not one of the containers. You can't place a form on a form. Later we will see how to create new forms should you need to do so.

2.13 Listing controls

Every control you place on a form is recorded in the form's Controls property. The first object is Controls[0], the second Controls[1], etc. The total number of objects on the form is given by Controls.Count.

Every control has a .ToString( ) method, which returns a string of information about the control. You can see all the names of the controls on a form with the following code. Place a button and a selection of controls on a form and add the following code for the button click:

```
for (int i = 0; i<this.Controls.Count; i++)
{
    MessageBox.Show("Control number "+i.ToString( ) + " is called" +
        this.Controls[i].Name);
}
```

The keyword 'this' refers to the current object, in this case the form. Again, we will see this later.

2.14 Exercise: Dating registration form

Let's create a registration form which might be used by a dating agency. We will just consider the design and controls, we won't write any code for this.

The form will have a tab control to select different pages for name, address and details of the person they would like to meet (WLTM).

On the Name tab, there will be TextBoxes for First name and Last Name, radio buttons to select gender (M or F) and a NumericUpDown control to select your age.

The Address tab will have TextBoxes for address and a scrollable list box to select a country (UK, Europe, USA, other).

The WLTM Details tab will have the following controls:
A panel control containing:
- A check box to select common interests (sports, pub, walking, dining out).
- Radio buttons to select age range of the person you would like to meet (range 18-25, 26-39, 40-59, 60+).

Start a new project, windows application and call it DatingForm.

Add the Tab Control

From the Containers Toolbox menu, select a TabControl and place it on the form. Resize it so that it takes up most of the form.

Change the headings. Click TabPages in the properties window; a small box with three dots appears (...); click this to display the TabPage collection editor. Here you can select the tab pages and change their Text and the TabPage name. They are currently called tabPage1 and tabPage2. Change their Text properties to Name and Address; you can leave their Name as tabPage1 and 2. Use the Add button to add a third tab page and call it WLTM, see figure 2.9. Close the collection editor.

Figure 2.9 The Tab Control

Add the details

Select the Name tab and add three labels and change their Text properties to suit (First Name, Last Name and Age). Add two textboxes for the name. Add a NumericUpDown control and change the minimum property to 18. The first tab should be similar to figure 2.10:

Name	Address	WLTM Details

First Name

Last Name

Age   18

Figure 2.10 Dating Form design - Name

Select the Address tab and add labels and text boxes for the address. Add a list box and add the countries mentioned above using Items collection properties. The design should be similar to figure 2.11:

Figure 2.11 Dating Form design - Address

Finally select the WLTM Details tab and add a GroupBox container to the form change its Text to Interest. Add four CheckBoxes to the GroupBox and change their Text to those mentioned above (or make up your own interests). Note that as they are all grouped together, you can move them around the form as a group.

The WLTM design should be similar to figure 2.12:

Figure 2.12 Dating Form design – WLTM

Save the project and run the program.

2.15 Self Assessment Exercises

1) Watch Lesson 2 of the Tier Two Beginner Series videos at:
   http://msdn.microsoft.com/en-gb/beginner/bb308734.aspx

2) Watch the supporting videos pointed to at Elektor's web site.

3) Experiment with the controls mentioned in section 2.10. Place them on a form and change their properties. If they have a collection of items (e.g. the combo box), add some items to the list and observe its operation.

4) The Tooltip control. The tooltip control provides a hint for your controls. Add a button and a toolTip control to the form (it will display in the status bar). A property 'Tooltip on Tooltip1' is now added to the button. Type a message for this property (e.g. 'Press me'), run the program and hold the mouse cursor over the button. Watch the message appear then disappear.

5) Keyboard entry. Add a textbox to a form. For its KeyDown event, add the following code:

```
if (e.KeyCode == Keys.Enter)
{
        MessageBox.Show("You pressed enter");
        textBox1.Clear();
}
```

6) Note that all the available key identifiers are displayed by the IntelliSense. See if you can find out what the EXSEL key is! Keyboard events and key identifiers are on the www.w3c.org web site.

7) Find a list of the escape (backslash) characters such as \r and \n and what they do.

8) Events. Try writing some code that executes on different events. For example try writing code for a MouseEnter and MouseLeave events for a control. They could be simple MessageBox.Show messages – 'Entered' and 'Left'

9) Find out how to use some other controls in the other tabs, such as the ToolStrip and StatusStrip in the Menus & Toolbars tab.

2.16 Summary

In this chapter we have looked at some of the common controls in more detail, including the button, textbox, list box, check box, radio button and their main properties and events. We have seen some of the other events such as Mouse and Keyboard events. Properties, events and methods are the basis of object oriented programming, which is covered later.

We have seen that the controls can be grouped together using containers and used these in a design exercise.

Chapter 3 - Dialogs and forms

3.1 Introduction

In the first chapters we saw that controls such as buttons, labels and text boxes are selected from the toolbox and placed on the form to design the user interface. We also saw that these controls had properties (e.g. height, position on the form), events (e.g. button click) and methods (e.g. Add, Insert and Remove). Now we will look at displaying messages and inputting values using dialogs and forms.

3.2 User messages - The Message Box Dialog

It's easy to display messages to your users. You will have seen messages boxes and prompts in windows applications. We shall see how to add them to our programs.

Dialogs are used to display information and if necessary accept some input or response. They are not controls you place on your form but appear when the program runs. You can use standard dialogs or create your own using forms.

The simplest way to display a message is to use a MessageBox, see figure 3.1. The code is simply MessageBox.Show followed by the string to be displayed, e.g.:

MessageBox.Show("Displayed using MessageBox.Show( );");

Figure 3.1 MessageBox.Show display

To try this, place a button on a form and insert the above code for the button click event. Click the button to display the message.

Note there is no caption. You can display a caption by adding a second string to the MessageBox.Show() method, e.g.:

MessageBox.Show("text","caption");

The Show( ) method can be extended further to add common response buttons such as Yes/No/Cancel, OK/Cancel, Abort/Retry/Ignore. You can also add an icon such as an exclamation mark from a selection of icons. To do this you add the message buttons and icon after the text and caption messages, for example:

MessageBox.Show("This will format your disk!", "Format caption", MessageBoxButtons.OKCancel, MessageBoxIcon.Exclamation);

Figure 3.2 shows how it is displayed.

Figure 3.2 MessageBox with response buttons

You can find out the button groups and icons by letting the C# IntelliSense prompt you with the options, see figure 3.3a and 3.3b.

Figure 3.3a and figure 3.3b MesssageBox Buttons and icons

As we have seen before, numbers are converted to strings automatically, you can type:

MessageBox.Show("You are "+25);

And to display multiple lines use \r and \n (they mean 'return' and 'new line'), for example:

MessageBox.Show("You are \r\n"+25);

You have no control over where the message box is placed. We shall see how we can design our own message box (using a new form) to do this later.

3.2.1 Message Reply

Of course we want to know which button is selected and we have to write code to deal with the button press.

The Show method returns a response value (a DialogResult) which indicates which button was pressed. This can then be used to determine the program's operation. The results are Abort, Cancel, Ignore, No, None, OK, Retry and Yes. They are preceeded with 'DialogResult', for example: DialogResult.Yes.

Exercise: Dealing with responses

Enter this code for a ButtonClick method and see what happens:

```
if (MessageBox.Show("This will format your disk!", "Formatting disk",
   MessageBoxButtons.OKCancel) == DialogResult.OK)
   {
     MessageBox.Show("Formatting disk");
   }
    else
   {
     MessageBox.Show("Did not format disk");
   }
```

Here the user's response is compared (using the '==' operation) and if the OK button is pressed the Dialog result is DialogResult.OK and formatting would take place otherwise (else) it does not format the disk.

Note what we have been doing with the simple MessageBox.Show( ) method. Initially we used it to display a message, but then the same method was extended to add a caption, buttons and icons. There are in fact 20 different ways of using the Show method. The IntelliSense knows about all of them and lists them as you type. This is called overloading and is one of the features of object oriented programming, and we shall see this later.

3.3 Creating your own dialogs - Prompting for input

The MessageBox.Show( ) is very versatile, but there is no method to prompt for input from the user. To do this you have to create your own message box using forms. We shall do this now as an exercise.

3.3.1 User input - Adding forms exercise

Start a new Windows application project and save it, calling it 'Forms'. Add a button to form1. Rename the button btnShowForm and give it a caption 'Show my dialog'.

Now we are going to create our custom dialog form. Add a new form to the project using Project> Add Windows Form and select Windows form. The new form appears. You might like to take this opportunity of seeing what else you can add, for example the standard Help> About Box can be added. For now use the default name of the form, Form2, see figure 3.4.

Figure 3.4. Adding a new form

Form2.cs[Design] tab appears. Controls can now be added to our second form. Change the Text property of the new form to 'Custom dialog box'.
Add a text box to the new form and change its properties as follows:

Name:	txtCustomMessage – let's give it a sensible name,
MultiLine:	True – let's allow many lines of text. Doing this gives you sizing handles, so make it almost fill the form.

Add some lines of text to the text box. Click the Text property and add the first line, click the down arrow and add more lines of text. Press Control and Enter to finish adding text.

Finally add buttons for the response. Add one with the text 'Cancel', and one with the text 'OK'. We want them to provide a response, so change their DialogResult property to 'Cancel' and 'OK' respectively. Select these from the drop down box in the DialogResult property, see figure 3.5.

Figure 3.5 Dialog Result options

Your design should be similar to Figure 3.6.

Figure 3.6 Custom Dialog Box

If we use the Show( ) method to display this form, the user can choose to ignore the form by closing it. This may not be desirable, for example for a password dialog. We will ensure the user must click one of the buttons to continue, so the ShowDialog( ) method will be used to display the form. This is known as a modal form.

Note that you don't have to write code to close the form, clicking the button will close it automatically.

Now we need to write the code to display our dialog box. Display form1 (double-click form1.cs in the solution explorer if it isn't displayed) and double-click the 'Show my dialog' button you added. Add the following code for the button click:

```
private void btnShowForm_Click(object sender, EventArgs e)
{
    Form2 dialogForm = new Form2( );
    if (dialogForm.ShowDialog( ) == DialogResult.OK)
```

```
        {
            MessageBox.Show("You clicked OK");
        }
        else
        {
            MessageBox.Show("You clicked Cancel");
        } // end if .. else
    } // end button Click
```

Note how we create and use Form2, we declare it in the first line and give it a name new name dialogForm. We use this name later in the code.

Run the program. Clicking the button should display form2. You can then click OK or Cancel. If you are having problems, check the DialogResult properties have been set correctly.

At this stage we have managed to show a second form, but haven't yet passed values between the forms (say the text in the text box). Before we do that, let's look at the timer component and 'splash' forms.

3.4 Splash forms and the Timer control

Now we know how to display a second form, we can display a 'splash' or advertising form that will show for a short time before the main application starts. We will use the timer control to close the form automatically.

Exercise: A splash form

Create a new application, call it Splash and create a directory for the solution. Double-click the form to display the default event, Form1_Load. Add the code below so that the event code is:

```
    private void Form1_Load(object sender, EventArgs e)
    {
        Form2 form2Show = new Form2( );      // create a new form 2
        form2Show.Show( );                   // and show it
    }
```

When form1 is loaded it will show form2 (when we've added it).

Now add a second form (Project > Add Windows Form > Windows Form). Use the default name (Form2). Add a label to form2 and change its caption property to 'Hello'.

Now add a timer control to form2. This is found in the toolbox Components group:

   Timer

The timer won't be seen at run-time (sometimes called a non-visual component). The timer icon will be displayed in the IDE's status bar. Its most used properties are:

Name : The usual meaning,
Enabled: True or False,
Interval : Time in milliseconds - default 100,
Tag : free for use by your application.

Change the timer's Enabled property to True and the Interval to 1000 (1 second)

The timer only has one event which is called Tick. The code written in the timer_Tick event runs every 'Interval' milliseconds when the timer is enabled. Double-click the timer icon and add the following code so the timer tick event becomes:

```
private void timer1_Tick(object sender, EventArgs e)
{
    this.Close();
}
```

Run the program and observe its operation. You may find that form2 is displayed behind form1. In this case, change form2's TopMost property to true and run the program again.

Form1 is the main form - it displays form2 when it is loaded. Form2 closes itself on the timer event.

Look again at the timer code: this.Close( ); Remember the keyword 'this' refers to the current object, in this case the form with the timer code.

Form events.

A form is only loaded once, but activated every time it is displayed. You can see this in action if you move the form load code to the form activated event. Display form1's events in the properties box and scroll to the Activated event. Click this to display the framework code for the Form1_Activated event and type in the form load code we used earlier. Run the program again. There will be lots of form2 boxes appearing. Be prepared to stop the program using Shift-F5!

3.5 Accessing controls on other forms

This is a bit complicated so early on in the book, so feel free to ignore for now and return to it later.

Now that we know how to create and display a second form, let's see how to access controls on the second form.

Remember when we add a form to our project, that's all we do. To display it we have to create an instance of it and show it. (That's what the form load code did in the last section). Any controls on a form are private to that form, so to access them from another form we either have to declare them public or preferably create and call a public method (you may know this as a procedure or subroutine) which accesses the object.

Let's suppose we have a form1 with a button, which when clicked will change the text in a textbox on form2.

The code for the button on Form1 is:

```
Form2 form2Show = new Form2( );
form2Show.setTextBox1("Hello");        // call the setTextBox method
                                       // in form2 to change the text
form2Show.Show( );                     // and show the form
```

Now create a <u>public</u> method on form2 which is called to change the (private to form1) textbox:

```
public void setTextBox1(string temp)
{
    this.textBox1.Text = temp;
}
```

Exercise - Accessing controls on other forms

- You can modify the splash program to try this.
- Add the 'form2Show.setTextBox1("Hello");' code to the form1 load event code.
- Add a textbox to form2 and add the setTextBox method code after the closing bracket for the timer tick code.
- Run the program. The textbox should display 'Hello'.

To do the opposite and access a control on form1 (say textbox1) from the second form, you have to add a method to access the text as above, but also provide a link for form2 to form1.

The method to change the textbox (in form1.cs) is as follows:

```
public void SetTextBox(string strText)
  {
    textBox1.Text = strText;
  }
```

Use 'this' to pass the link for form2 it is created. Add the following to Form1_Load:

```
private void Form1_Load(object sender, EventArgs e)
```

```
        {
          new Form2(this).Show();
        }
```

You could also modify the code we used before to:

```
        Form2 form2Show = new Form2(this);
```

We are now passing some information when form2 is created, so change the code at the top of form2 to:

```
        public partial class Form2 : Form
        {
          Form1 parent;
          public Form2(Form1 p)
                // form1 is passed as 'this' and is referenced by 'p' - parent
          {
            InitializeComponent();
            parent = p;
          }
```

For form2's button click, change the code to the following:

```
        private void button1_Click(object sender, EventArgs e)
        {
          parent.SetTextBox("hello there");
          // this will call the SetTextBox method on the creating form – form1
        }
```

Click the button on form2 and form1's textbox text should change.

3.6 Random numbers

To use random numbers a Random object must be created (instantiated). Having done that it methods are used to obtain the random numbers. To instantiate a random object, use the following code:

```
        Random rndObject = new Random( );     // declare a random object
```

To get a random integer number, use the Random.Next() method.

has three possibilities:

```
        1)  randomObj.Next( );
```

This returns a non-negative random number:

int intRandom = rndObj.Next();

2) randomObj.Next(int max);

This returns a value from 0 to max-1:

int intRandom = rndObj.Next(5);   // random number 0 - 4

3) randomObj.Next(int min, int max);

This returns a value between min and max-1:

int intRandom = rndObj.Next(3,7);   // number from 3 to 6

If you want the number to have a specified seed, use the following:

Random rndSeed = new Random(seed);   // seed is an integer

You can obtain a floating point random number using rndObj.NextDouble() which returns a value equal or greater than 0.0 but less than 1, as follows:

double randomDouble = rndObj.NextDouble();   // gives 0 - 0.99999
// or
double randomDouble = 15 + 10*rndObj.NextDouble();   // gives 15 - 24.999

You can't pass a value to this method.

We'll use these in the following self assessment exercises.

3.7 Self Assessment Exercises

1. Snap game using Timers and the Random object

This exercise randomly displays different colours in a picture box and displays a message if the colours are the same. It uses timers and picture boxes and introduces random numbers. Start a new project and:

- Place a Timer from the component palette on the form. This will not show at run-time. When the timer code runs it will check for a snap and generate new colours. Make sure its properties are: Enabled = True and Interval = 500 (1/2 second).

- Add two Pictureboxes to the form. Change their BackColor property to Web>Red. Our program will change their colour and display a Message box if they compare.

Find the C# code:

```
public partial class Form1 : Form
```

After the open curly bracket { and before the code: 'public Form1( )', add the following to declare a Random object and an integer identifier to hold the number:

```
Random randomColour = new Random( );      // declare a random object
int randomNumber;                          // integer to hold a random number
```

Double-click the timer component and enter the following code between the curly brackets:

```
if (pictureBox1.BackColor == pictureBox2.BackColor)
{
    timer1.Enabled = false;         // if colours are the same stop the timer
    MessageBox.Show("Snap!");       // and display message
    timer1.Enabled = true;          // start timer when message is OKed
}

// Generate new colours
randomNumber = randomColour.Next(3);       // random number 0 to 2
// change pictureBox1 colour
if (randomNumber == 0) pictureBox1.BackColor = Color.Blue;
if (randomNumber == 1) pictureBox1.BackColor = Color.Green;
if (randomNumber == 2) pictureBox1.BackColor = Color.Red;

randomNumber = randomColour.Next(3);       // random number 0 to 2
// change pictureBox2 colour
if (randomNumber == 0) pictureBox2.BackColor = Color.Blue;
if (randomNumber == 1) pictureBox2.BackColor = Color.Green;
if (randomNumber == 2) pictureBox2.BackColor = Color.Red;
```

Run the program and see how it works. We will look at the 'if' statement soon. Note how the random object has to be instantiated and then a number generated and saved in an integer variable.

2. Extend the program to

1) Add a second timer with a different Interval to control the second picture box.

2) Add a button and a text box for the user to play Snap. The user is to click the button when they see a snap. The text box will contain the score. Increment a counter if the player guesses correctly and decrement it if it is incorrect or a Snap is missed. The counter could be a value in a text box; you will have to convert its text from a string to an integer to increment the number.

3) Add a stop/stop button to control the program. If its caption is 'Start', change it from 'Start' to 'Stop and enable the timer, otherwise (else) change its caption (from Stop) to Start and disable the timer. You will have to use an 'if .. then .. else' statement:

```
if (StartStopButton.Text == "Start")
{
    // change caption to Stop and enable timer
}
else
{
    // change caption to Start and disable timer
}
```

4) Fully debug and test the program. E.g. can the user guess more than once for a match?

3.8 Summary

This chapter has covered using the MessageBox dialog to display simple messages and dealing with the button click response. Some of the many MessageBox possibilities were seen. This type of code is called overloading.

We saw how to design and display our own forms. This was taken further to design a splash form which introduced the non-visual timer control. We also covered how to access objects on one form from another.

In the self assessment exercises, by designing a snap game, the random object was introduced.

Chapter 4 - The C# Language - the basics

4.1 Introduction

As well as designing our user interface we have to write some code. We will start by looking at the basic data types, assignments and comparisons. In the next chapter we will look at decision making with control and program flow.

4.2 Declarations - Variables and data type identifiers.

All variables used in our programs must have a data type and a name or identifier. Before we can use a variable or constant its data type (e.g. integer, floating point, string) and its name must be declared. This can be done at any time before (or when) the variable is used.

A variable is declared by stating its data type followed by its name. It can optionally be given an initial value. We saw the following declaration in Chapter 2:

```
string strMessage = "Cancel";
```

This declares a string data type called strMessage with the initial value "Cancel".

Constants are defined by adding the reserved word const, for example:

```
const float GOLDENRATIO = 1.61803399F;
```

You must declare an initial value for a constant.

C# supports nine integral data types, two floating point types, a type suitable for financial calculations, types for characters and strings and a type for Boolean logical variables (true and false). The data types and example declarations are shown in table 4.1.

Data type	Example declaration	Description
byte	byte eightBits = 128;	0 to 255
sbyte	sbyte signedByte = -128;	-128 to +127
short	short signedWord = 32767;	-32768 to 32767
int	int bigNumber = 1234567;	-2147483648 to +2147483647
long	long evenBigger = 12345678;	Large integer
float	float fltNumber = 0.23F;	Approx. -3.4E38 to +3.4E38
double	double dblFloatingPoint = 2.345D;	Approx -1.79E208 to +1.79E208
decimal	decimal decMoney = 3.33M;	Used for currency
bool	bool bolTrueFalse = true;	TRUE or FALSE
char	char chrA = 'A';	Letters of the alphabet : 'A' or '*'
string	string strAString = "this is a string";	Contained in double quotes
uint	uint uintLarge = 543210;	Unsigned, 0 to 4,294,967,295

| ushort | ushort ushtMedium = 43210; | Unsigned, 0 to 65535 |
| ulong | ulong ulngLong = 0; | Unsigned, 0 to 10^{20} |

Table 4.1 C# data types

The keyword var can also be used leaving the compiler to determine the data type. The following two declarations are equivalent:

```
int    i = 10;      // explicitly declared
var    i = 10;      // implicitly declared (will be Int32)
```

Of course variables declared using var must be initialized.

4.2.1 Naming convention

As we have said it is a good idea to adopt a convention when naming your variables, constants and (when we come to them) methods and class names, so that by just looking at the name you know what they are. I have already suggested you use three letters to indicate the type of control placed on a form, e.g. btn, lbl, txt etc.

You can of course use your own rules, but by convention variables start with a lowercase letter separating each word with a capital letter. e.g. loopCount, moneyOwed and classes will begin with a capital letter, e.g. CalculateSine, SquareNumber. It's common to use all capital letters for constants.

Preferred naming conventions can be found by searching for 'C# naming convention' on the MSDN site at http://msdn.microsoft.com

4.2.2 Some declaration examples:

Here are some examples of declaring variables and constants:

```
const double MYCONSTANT = 2.14159;
const int MAXSIZE = 10, MINSIZE = 1;  // more than one in a line
const ushort HEXNUMBER = 0xFFFF;   // 0x used for hexadecimal

int integerNumber;                       // not initialized
double temperature = 98.6; freezing = 0.0;     // two at once
char letterA;                            // a character
bool lightSwitch = true;                 // a Boolean – true or false
```

4.3 Assignments and operators

Assignments are made with the equals symbols '=' and end with a semicolon, for example

Example: sum = one + two;

The usual operators are used: add +, subtract -, multiply *, divide / and remainder %, as is the order of their operation (precedence): Unary (e.g. 'not'), brackets, division and multiplication, add and subtract.

4.3.1 Shortcuts

Variables can be incremented and decremented using the shortcuts '++' and '--'. These operators can be put both before and after the variable to be changed. You can have x++ or ++x. In most cases it doesn't make any difference, but if you are assigning the value to another variable, it will. For instance the following code displays the value 0.

```
int x;
int y = 0;
x = y++;                        // assign to x then increment y
MessageBox.Show(x.ToString());
```

Whereas this code displays the value 1:

```
int x;
int y = 0;
x = ++y;                        // increment y, then assign y to x
MessageBox.Show(x.ToString());
```

In both cases, y ends up with the value 1.

Assignments such as x=x+y; can be shortened as well. In this case to x+=y; Note that it's not shortened to x=+y;. This is useful for objects with long names.

The shortened versions are:

```
add = add + 3;              becomes      add += 3;
div = div / 4;              becomes      div /= 4;
mult = mult * 5;            becomes      mult *= 5;
sub = sub - 2;              becomes      sub -= 2;
remainder = remainder%4;    becomes      remainder %= 4;
```

4.4 Comments

```
/*
Slash-star is a multi-line comment- it is ended with a star-slash
*/
// or you can use a double slash which ignores the rest of the line
```

You can comment (or uncomment) sections of selected code using the following icons:

4.5 Casting (converting) data types

You may find that you have to convert from one data type to another to perform an operation. We have already seen conversions from numbers to strings. Conversions can be implicit or explicit.

Implicit conversions are done automatically and guarantee that no data is lost in the conversion. For instance you can convert a single precision 'float' data type to 'double' without a problem because the double encompasses the float. However if you try to convert a double precision variable to single precision some data may be lost and you have to explicitly say that it's OK. Consider the following code:

```
double dbli=1.234;   // declare a double precision number
float fltj=1.234F;    // declaration a single precision floating-point number
dbli = fltj;          // is OK you can convert float to double
fltj = dbli;          // this errors – it requires an explicit cast
```

The 'double' data type has more precision than 'float', so the line of code 'fltj = dbl;'errors, requesting an explicit cast. If you only require a result to single precision, then you can explicitly say the change is OK but placing (float) in front of 'dbli', as follows:

```
fltj = (float) dbli;      // the (float) indicates that you say it's OK
```

Table 4.2 shows a list of safe conversions:

Data type	Can be converted to
byte	char, short, int, long, float, double, decimal
short	int, long, float, double, decimal
int	long, float, double, decimal
long	float, double, decimal
float	double, decimal
double	decimal

Table 4.2 Safe data type conversions

Integer divides are automatically truncated, e.g:

```
integerNumber = 124 / 3;
MessageBox.Show(integerNumber.ToString( ));        // displays 41
integerNumber = integerNumber % 3;
MessageBox.Show(integerNumber.ToString( ));  // remainder
```

4.6 Characters and strings

Characters are declared by using a single quote around the character and strings defined using double quotes. As we have seen, strings that represent a number (e.g. a number typed into a text box) can be converted using the Parse method such as float.Parse(string) or int.Parse(string). Examples are:

```
char chrCapitalA = 'A';
string strAString = "this is a string";
string strOneChar = "a";          // a one character string!
string strNumber = "1.234";
float fltNumber =  float.Parse(strNumber);
int integerNumber = int.Parse("123");
int intNumber = (int)Math.Round(float.Parse(strNumber));
```

To incorporate the double-quote character in a string, it is preceded with a backslash character. We have already seen this in section 2.3.1, where we used \r and \n to represent the non-printing characters 'return' and 'new line'.

4.7 Escape sequences

These are called escape sequences. Some of the more common escape sequences are:

Character	ASCII representation	ASCII value	Escape sequence
Newline	LF	10 or 0x0a	\n
Carriage return	CR	13 or 0x0d	\r
Backslash	\	92 or 0x5c	\\
Single quote	'	39 or 0x27	\'
Double quote	"	34 or 0x22	\"

4.8 Logical operations - Boolean data type

The Boolean data type (bool) is used in cases where only true or false conditions exist. Logic operations can be performed on Boolean and other data types. The logic operations are 'NOT', 'AND', 'OR' and 'XOR' - exclusive or, and are performed with the symbols: !, &, |, and ^. The logic operations are shown in Table 4.3.

A	B	!A	A & B	A | B	A ^ B
		NOT	AND	OR	EXOR
0	0	1	0	0	0
0	1	1	0	1	1
1	0	0	0	1	1
1	1	0	1	1	0

Table 4.3 Logic Operations

Example:

```
bool A = false;
bool B = false;
bool AexclusiveOrB;
AexclusiveOrB = (!A & B) | (A & !B);
// or use
AexclusiveOrB = A ^ B;
```

4.9 Mathematical Functions

C# provides a Math class. Some of the more common Math tasks are shown below.

Name	Description
Abs	Returns the absolute value of a number, greater than a minimum and less than a maximum.
Example:	`decimal absA = Math.Abs(-3.141M);` // absA is 3.141
Acos, Asin, Atan	Returns the angle in radians for the (cos, sin or tan) of the number.
	`double x = 0.707;` // -1< x <1
	`double theta = Math.Acos(x);` // theta = 0.7855491..
Sin, Cos, Tan	Returns the sine, cosine, tangent of an angle measured in radians.
	`double theta = 0.7855491;`
	`double sine = Math.Asin(theta);` // sine = 0.903582..
Cosh, Sinh, Tanh	Returns the hyperbolic (cosine, sine or tangent) of an angle.
	`double theta = 0.707;`
	`double tanh = Math.Tanh(theta);` // tanh = 0.608792..
Exp	Returns e raised to the specified power.
	`double power = 0.5;`
	`double eToPower = Math.Exp(power);` // power = 1.648..
IEEERemainder	Returns the remainder from the division of two numbers.
	`double rem = Math. IEEERemainder (22.3, 7.0);` // 1.300..
Log	Returns the natural logarithm of a specified number.
	`double ln2 = Math.Log(2.0);` // 0.6931..
Log10	Returns the base 10 logarithm of a specified number.
	`double log2 = Math.Log(2.0);` // 0.3010..
Max	Returns the larger of two specified numbers.

```
double max = Math.Max(2.0, 3.0);        // 3.0
```

Min
Returns the smaller of two numbers.
```
double min = Math.Min(2.0, 3.0);        // 2.0
```

Pow
Returns a number raised to a specified power.
```
double eight = Math.Pow(2.0,3.0);       // 8.0
```

Round
Rounds a value to the nearest integer or number of decimal places.
```
double round = Math.Round(12.501);  // 13
```

Sqrt
Returns the square root of a specified number.
```
double sqrt = Math.Sqrt(3.0);  // 1.732..
```

Truncate
Calculates the integral part of a number.
```
double trunc = Math.Truncate(12.501);  // 12
```

There are many variations of these, for more details, refer to the Microsoft library at:

http://msdn.microsoft.com/en-us/library/4zfefwz9(v=VS.100).aspx

4.10 Date and Time

The DateTime structure is split into a date part and a time part. The date holds a date, month and year and the time holds hours, minutes, seconds and milliseconds. The smallest interval between two DateTime values is one hundred nanoseconds and is called a tick.

DateTime is a structure, and you have to instantiate it before you can use it as follows:

```
DateTime theTime = new DateTime( );
// or
DateTime xmas2007 = new DateTime(2007, 12, 25);
        // will also contain time – Midnight
```

You can also set the hours and minutes using:

```
DateTime newDate = new DateTime(2001, 2, 3, 4, 5, 6, 7);
        // 3 Feb 2001 04:05:06.0007
```

The current date and time can be found by using the property 'Now'. A difference (a time span) is calculated using TimeSpan:

```
// declare Xmas 2007
DateTime xmas2007 = new DateTime(2007, 12, 25);
DateTime theTime = new DateTime( );
```

```
theTime = DateTime.Now;                          // get time now
label1.Text = theTime.ToString( );
TimeSpan tspan = theTime - xmas2007;          // difference?
int daysToXmas = tspan.Days;     // also .Hours, .Minutes, .Seconds etc.
label2.Text = "Time since Christmas 2007 =  " + tspan.ToString( );
label3.Text = "Days since Christmas 2007 =  " + tspan.Days.ToString( );
```

4.10.1 DateTime properties and methods

You might want to extract the date or time from a DateTime object. Some of the DateTime properties are:

Month	xmas2007.Month	// returns 12
Day	xmas2007.Day	// returns 25
DayOfWeek	xmas2007.DayOfWeek	// returns DayOfWeek.Tuesday

The DateTime class also contains methods such as:

Add	adds a timespan	
AddDays	Adds a number of days	xmas2007.AddDays(7); // new year
AddYears	Adds a number of years	xmas2007.AddYears(1); // xmas2008

There are also AddMilliseconds, AddSeconds, AddMonths and others.

4.11 Scope

The scope of an identifier (such as a variable or method) refers to the region of code where it exists and can be accessed. The scope can be block or class scope. Generally, classes have public scope and methods and variables have private scope. The public and private keywords allow you to override these defaults. They can only be used at the class level, not within a method.

4.11.1 Block scope

When an identifier is declared within a block of code or method, i.e. within curly brackets, it is given block scope. It is then accessible within the block but not outside it. For instance:

```
if (true)
{
  int blockVariable=0;              // blockVariable only exists here.
}
// blockVariable not accessible here
```

The block can be a block within curly brackets as above or a method such as a button click.

4.11.2 Class scope

The class code starts after the open curly bracket after the class statement, e.g.:

```
public class Form1 : Form
{
        // class code and scope starts here.
```

Identifiers declared at this level are accessible by all the code within the class.

The following code may help explain the scope of some variables.

```
public class Form1 : Form
// class Form1 is public and accessible to other classes.

{
    int ClassVariable;          // accessible within this class
    private void button1_Click(object sender, EventArgs e)
    {
        int MethodVariable1;          // accessible only in this button click
        ClassVariable = 3;            // is OK
        {                             // new block of code
            int BlockVariable;        // only exists in this block
            MethodVariable1 = 0;      // is OK
            BlockVariable = 1;        // is OK
        }
        BlockVariable = 2;            // is an error
    }

    private void button2_Click(object sender, EventArgs e)
    {
        int MethodVariable2;          // accessible only in this method
        ClassVariable = 4;            // is OK
        MethodVariable2 = 1;          // is OK
        MethodVariable1 = 5;          // is an error
    }
}
```

You should use private scope where possible, otherwise it makes programs more difficult to understand and debug.

We shall see more on scope when we look at the chapters on methods and objects.

For more examples on scope see the self assessment exercises.

4.12 Self Assessment Exercises

1. Watch the Microsoft Tier Two beginner's Lesson 4 video at:
    http://msdn.microsoft.com/en-gb/beginner/bb308734.aspx

2. Watch the supporting videos pointed to at Elektor's web site.

3. Variables
Declare variables with different data types. Try to assign them to each other and see the error messages. Where possible try to cast from one data type to another.

Declare some variables in one button click code and see if they can be accessed by separate button click code.

4. Scope.
Investigate scope. Place two buttons on a form and change their button click code as follows. Note the regions of code where the string variables exist.

```
public partial class Form1 : Form
{
    string strClassString = "ClassString";

    private void button1_Click(object sender, EventArgs e)
    {
        string strMethodString = "MethodString";
        MessageBox.Show(strMyClassString);    // is OK
        MessageBox.Show(strMethodString);     // is OK
    }

    private void button2_Click(object sender, EventArgs e)
    {
        MessageBox.Show(strClassString);    // is OK
        MessageBox.Show(strMethodString);  // will error

    }
```

Find out in which regions of code you can declare the strings as public or private.

Declare a second strClassString on the first line of the button2_Click code as follows, and see what happens.

```
string strClassString = "newString";
```

This is a different strClassString from the first one declared.

5. DateTime exercise. Write a program that works out how many days there are until your birthday.

4.13 Summary

This chapter has covered the basic C# language constructs of data types, assignment and casting or converting data types. Characters and strings have been seen as well as mathematical and logic operations. Further concepts, such as scope and more detailed data types such as DateTime have also been covered.

Chapter 5 - The C# Language - arrays, structures and strings

5.1 Introduction

In this chapter we will cover arrays and strings. Arrays enable us to hold many items of the same data type. Strings are arrays of characters. We shall see how to declare arrays and strings and see some of the methods associated with them. We shall also see how to declare and use variable size, or dynamic, arrays.

5.2 Arrays

Arrays are used to hold a number of items of the same type of data, e.g. a list of peoples' ages, birth dates or salary. To declare an array put square brackets '[ ]' after the data type and then set its size, as follows:

```
int[ ] intArray;              // an integer array called intArray.
intArray = new int[20];       // create array with 20 items – from 0 to 19
```

This can be done in one line of code:

```
int[ ] intArray = new int[20];
```

You can also declare and fill the array with data as follows. The size of the array is calculated from the number of items.

```
int[ ] intArray = { 1, 2, 3, 4, 5 };
double[ ] dblArray = { 1.0, -2.0, 3.0 };
string[ ] arrayOfNames = { "Peter", "Paul", "Mary" };
```

Individual items in an array are accessed using a number in the square brackets. The item within the square brackets is known as the index and can be an expression. The index starts at zero; hence the last index is the size of the array minus one. Using the array declared above, for example:

```
intArray[0] = 5;                      // sets the first element to 5
intArray[1] = intArray[6*3+1];        // copy the last element [19]
                                      // to the second element
```

If your program accesses an index outside the size of the array, then a run-time error message will occur. If you don't know how large your array needs to be, you can either create one that you know will be large enough or use a dynamic array type which automatically changes its size to suit. We shall see how to do this later.

Arrays have properties, the most useful of which is 'Length' which, as it suggests, provides the length of the array. Hence the last item's index is always Length-1. For example:

```
intArray[intArray.Length-1] = 25;          // set the last element
```

Arrays also have methods. Some of these may not work as you think they might. Some examples are:

- Average – computes the average of the array
  Example: double dblAverage = intArray.Average();

- Contains – returns true or false if value is in array or not
  Example:
  ```
  if (intArray.Contains(3)) MessageBox.Show("contains '3'");
  ```

- Copy – copies an array, or part of an array starting at an index
  Example:
  ```
  int[ ] intArray = { 1, 2, 3, 4, 5 };
  int[ ] intArrayCopy = {-1,-1,-1,-1};
  intArrayCopy.CopyTo(intArray, 1);          // copy from index 1
  // intArray now contains 1, -1,-1,-1,-1
  ```

- BinarySearch – This uses a binary search to find an object in an array. This means the array must be sorted. If the item is not found a negative value is returned, otherwise the index of the item is returned.
  Example:
  ```
  double[ ] dblArray = { 1.0, 2.1, 3.2, 4.3, 5.4 };
  double lookingFor = 2.1;
  int indexIs = Array.BinarySearch(dblArray, (object)lookingFor);
  if (indexIs > 0) MessageBox.Show("Index is = " + indexIs);
  // finds 2.1 at index 1
  // but if array is reversed, e.g. 5.4, 4.3, 3.2, 2.1, 1.0
  // value 2.1 is NOT found
  ```

- Reverse – Reverses the elements in the array or portion of the array.
  Example:
  ```
  double[ ] dblArray = { 1.0, 2.1, 3.2, 4.3, 5.4 };
  Array.Reverse(dblArray);
  // dblArray now contains:  5.4, 4.3, 3.2, 2.1, 1.0
  ```

Note that 'Array.Reverse' is used, not 'dblArray.Reverse'.

- Sort – Sorts the elements in an array. This does not sort how you might expect. In the following example the result of the sort is 1, 111, 12, 2. It is not 1, 2, 12, 111.
  Example:
  ```
  string[ ] strArray = { "1", "12", "2", "111" };
  Array.Sort(strArray);
  // strArray now contains 1, 111, 12, 2
  ```

More details on array methods can be found at:

http://msdn.microsoft.com/en-us/library/system.array_methods(v=VS.71).aspx

5.3 Multidimensional arrays

Multidimensional arrays, i.e. ones with more than one index can be also be defined. For example a two dimensional array of students' scores would be defined by:

```
int [ , ] score;            // declare 2D array of integer data type
score = new int[3,2];       // set size 3 rows by 2 columns
```

This creates an array of three indexes (three students) each with two items, as follows:

	Exam 1	Exam 2
Student 1	score[0,0]	score[0,1]
Student 2	score[1,0]	score[1,1]
Student 3	score[2,0]	score[2,1]

To set the array values use the code:

```
score[0,1] = 68;      // Set exam 2 mark of student 1.
```

Two dimensional arrays can also be defined and initialised in one go, as follows:

```
double [ , ] twoDArray = { { 0.1, 1.1 }, { 2.1, 3.1 }, { 4.1, 5 } };
// is the same as
double [ , ] twoDArray = new double[3, 2]
            {{ 0.1, 1.1 }, { 2.1, 3.1 }, { 4.1, 5 }} ;
```

This can be extended to three and more dimensions as follows:

```
int[ , , ] my3Darray;
my3Darray = new int[2, 3, 4];
my3Darray[1, 2, 3] = 2;

int[ , , , ] my4Darray;
my4Darray = new int[2, 3, 4, 5];
my4Darray[1, 2, 3, 4] = 6;
```

You can also define multidimensional arrays with irregular sizes. These are known as jagged arrays. The following code shows how an array with 2, 4 and 6 elements may be created:

```
int[ ][ ] jagArray = new int[3][ ];        // create multidimensional array
jagArray [0] = new int [2];
jagArray [1] = new int [4];
jagArray [2] = new int [6];
jagArray[0][1] = 9;                        // last in array [0]
jagArray[1][3] = 10;                       // last in array [1]
jagArray[2][5] = 11;                       // last in array [2]
```

Each jagArray[ ] holds a reference to a single-dimensional integer array.

5.4 Structures

You might want to create a simple array that contains different data types. For instance, you might want a list of employees which contains their name, age and gender, salary etc. This is called a structure, but is also known as a record.

The individual data types in the structure are declared along with a way of accessing and changing their values. We will see this in more detail when we cover classes, but for now let's look at an example.

A structure is defined using the keyword 'struct'. The data types are declared then followed by a way of accessing them. The keyword 'this' is used to access the data. In your program you can create (or instantiate) as many versions of the structure as you want and 'this' refers to each individual version instantiated. An example personnel record structure might be as follows:

```
struct personnelRecord
{                                // declare the data types
    public string name;
    public int age;
    public double salary;
    public char gender;

// Provide access to the data.
// Note the same name (personnelRecord) is used

    public personnelRecord(string name, int age,
                        double salary, char gender)
    {
        this.name = name;
        this.age = age;
        this.salary = salary;
        this.gender = gender;
    }
} // end declaration of struct
```

This has only declared the structure it still needs to be instantiated in our program using the 'new' keyword, as we did with arrays. The structure must be declared at the top of the class, e.g. after the line of code: public class Form1 : Form {

A personnel list array of type personnelRecord is instantiated and its elements accessed as follows:

```
// one structure:
personnelRecord  myEmployees = new personnelRecord( );
myEmployees.age = 21;
myEmployees.gender = 'M';

// array of 10:
personnelRecord[ ] personnelList = new personnelRecord[10];
personnelList[0].name = "John Allwork";
personnelList[9].salary = 9999.99;
```

Note we use the dot notation to access the data just as we did with properties for our controls.

You might want to have some actions for your personnel such as change name or increase age or salary – these would be its methods. This leads us to classes and object oriented programming, which we will cover later.

5.4.1 The public declaration

We covered the public keyword briefly in the previous chapter. In the above code we have declared the individual variables in the structure as 'public'. If we had not done this, the items would only exist within the structure's block of code (within the curly brackets). Obviously we want to use these items outside the structure and declaring them as public allows this to happen. We will cover this in more detail in the chapters on classes and objects.

See the self assessment exercises for more on structures.

5.5 Character arrays and strings

Characters are variables of type char that hold a keyboard character (e.g. letters, numbers and symbols). Characters are held in UTF-8 format, which enables any language character to be used and is backward compatible with ASCII. Strings are a special type of array that holds characters.

As we have seen the data held in a text box is a string and individual characters from a text box can be treated as an array element as follows:

```
char chrText;                          // declare a char
chrText = textBox1.Text[2];            // read 3rd character from textbox
```

```
textBox1.Text = chrText.ToString( );     // convert char to string
                                         // and display in textbox
```

Note the conversion from the char to the string to allow us to write back to the text box.

You can declare an array of chars as follows:

```
char[ ] charArray;
charArray = new chr[20];   // 20 elements in the array - index 0 to 19
// or
char[ ] chrArray = { 'a', 'b', 'c', 'd' };
chrArray[2] = '4';              // change 'c' to '4'
```

5.6 String manipulation

C# .NET provides a number of methods to manipulate strings such as compare, split, search, change case etc.

We have already seen how we can concatenate strings (add one string onto the end of another) using the + operator, e.g.:

```
MessageBox.Show("This string has" + " this string added to it");
```

Of course the strings could have been previously declared and used as follows:

```
string string1 = "This string has";
string string2 = " this string added to it";
MessageBox.Show(string1 + string2);
```

We can determine the length of a string with the Length property:

```
int intLength;
string strOfChars = "This string has 29 characters";
intLength = strOfChars.Length;
MessageBox.Show(intLength.ToString( ));     // will display 29
```

Or we could have had:

```
MessageBox.Show((("This string has 29 characters").Length).ToString( ));
```

5.7 String conversion

Just to remind you how to convert between strings and numbers, you can convert from integers or floating point numbers to strings using the .ToString method:

```
int i = 10;
```

74

```
float f = 123456.22f;
double d = 123.567;
MessageBox.Show("int= " +i.ToString( )+"float= " +
        f.ToString( )+"double= "+d.ToString( ));
```

To convert from a string to a number, use the Parse method. There are many Parse methods. int.Parse and Int32.Parse convert from a string to an integer and float.Parse and double.Parse convert from a string to a floating point number, etc. For example:

```
string strFpNo = "123456.22";
string strIntNo = "12345";
MessageBox.Show("decimal= " + decimal.Parse(strFpNo));
MessageBox.Show("float= " + float.Parse(strFpNo));
MessageBox.Show("integer= " + int.Parse(strIntNo));
```

5.8 String methods
5.8.1 The Substring( ) method.

Part of a string can be retrieved using the Substring( ) method. The start position and number of characters is passed to the method and it returns the string. The first character is 0. For example:

```
MessageBox.Show(("Mary had a little lamb").Substring(2,5));
        // displays 'ry ha'
MessageBox.Show(("Mary had a little lamb").Substring(0,4));
        // displays 'Mary'
```

5.8.2 The IndexOf( ) and IndexOfAny( ) methods.

You can determine if one string is contained within another using the IndexOf( ) method. The string you wish to find is passed to the method and it returns the index of the string or -1 if it isn't found. This method is case sensitive. For example:

```
MessageBox.Show(("Mary had a little lamb").IndexOf("ry ha").ToString( ));
// displays 2
MessageBox.Show(("Mary had a little lamb").IndexOf("mar").ToString( ));
// displays -1. "mar" not found
```

This method can also be called with an integer starting index and a number of characters to search. For example:

- IndexOf(searchString);
- IndexOf(searchString, startIndex);
- IndexOf(searchString, startIndex, numberOfCharsToSearch);

Some examples are:

```
MessageBox.Show(("Mary had a lamb").IndexOf("ry ha",1).ToString( ));
// finds 'ry ha' at second index and displays 2

MessageBox.Show(("Mary had a lamb").IndexOf("ry ha",6).ToString( ));
// starts searching at position 6, doesn't find 'ry ha', and displays -1

MessageBox.Show(("Mary had a lamb").IndexOf("ry ha",1,2).ToString( ));
// starts at postion 1, looks for 2 characters,
// doesn't find 'ry ha' and displays -1

MessageBox.Show(("Mary had a lamb").IndexOf("ry ha",1,6).ToString( ));
// starts at postion 1, looks for 6 characters, finds 'ry ha' and displays 2
```

The IndexOfAny( ) method returns the first occurrence of any letters specified in a char array. For example:

```
string letters = "abcedfghijkl";
char[ ] searchLetters = { 'c', 'A', '$' };
letters.IndexOfAny(searchLetters);                    // finds 'c' at index 2.
```

The methods LastIndexOf( ) and LastIndexOfAny( ) perform the same operations but start at the end of the string.

5.8.3 Dealing with spaces - the Trim and Remove methods

The IndexOf( ) method could be used to find spaces, but the following methods are available to deal with spaces:

```
Trim( )        Removes spaces from the beginning and end of a string.
TrimEnd( )     Removes spaces from the end of a string.
TrimStart( )   Removes spaces from the beginning of a string.
Remove( )      Removes a specified number of spaces from a position in a string
```

5.8.4 The Replace method

Strings can easily be replaced using the Replace( ) method. The text to be replaced and the replacing text are both passed to the method. The string is searched and the text replaced. For example:

```
string strMaryText = "Mary had a little lamb";
MessageBox.Show(strMaryText);
string strReplacedText = strMaryText.Replace("little lamb", "black sheep");
MessageBox.Show(strReplacedText);
```

Note that all occurrences are replaced, so the following code replaces every letter 'a' with the letter 'i':

```
string strMaryText = "Mary had a little lamb";
MessageBox.Show(strMaryText);
string strReplacedText = strMaryText.Replace("a", "i");
MessageBox.Show(strReplacedText);
// displays Miry hid i little limb
```

5.8.5 The Split method - parsing strings

Strings can be parsed and individual words extracted by using the Split( ) method. This uses delimiter characters as markers. This method takes an array of chars containing the chars to be used as delimiters, e.g. spaces, commas colons etc. and the individual words between these are extracted.

The following code uses the delimiter characters space, comma, full stop, colon and tab to extract the individual words from the string: 'Delimiters are:colon\ttab space,comma.fullStop end'

It displays the original text and finds 8 words as shown in figures 5.1 and 5.2. It then displays them individually.

```
char[ ] delimiterChars = { ' ', ',', '.', ':', '\t' };
//delimiter characters are: space,comma,full stop,colon and tab

string text = "Delimiters are:colon\ttab space,comma.fullStop end";
MessageBox.Show("Original text: "+ text);

string[ ] words = text.Split(delimiterChars);
MessageBox.Show("Number of words in text:"+ words.Length);

foreach (string s in words)          // we'll see the foreach statement later
{
    MessageBox.Show(s);
}
```

Figure 5.1 Delimiter text

Figure 5.2 Number of words found

5.8.6 Upper and lower case methods

The ToUpper( ) and ToLower( ) methods convert a string to upper case and to lower case respectively. For instance:

        text=text.ToUpper();

5.9 Dynamic Arrays. The ArrayList Class

Dynamic arrays change their size as required as the program runs. They are implemented using an ArrayList. The array list is found in the System.Collections namespace (or library) and an ArrayList called arrayOfItems is declared as follows:

    System.Collections.ArrayList arrayOfItems =
            new System.Collections.ArrayList( );

If you add 'using System.Collections;' at the top of your code, you can dispense with it here.

You do not have to specify a data type for an ArrayList; any data type can be stored at any index in one. They also have properties and methods. The most useful property is Count. The Add and Remove methods are used to add and remove items from the list. They can be searched to see if they contain a particular item, and also cleared. As any data type can be stored in an ArrayList, a GetType( ) method can be used if you need to know what the data type is. A list of the more important properties and methods is shown in Table 5.1.

Property	Description
Capacity	Set or get the maximum size
Count	Gets the number of elements in the arraylist
Method	
Add	Adds an item to the end of the list
Clear	Deletes all the elements from the list
Contains	Determines if an element is in the list
Insert	Inserts an element at the specific index

Remove	Removes first occurrence of the object
ToArray	Copies the arraylist to an array

Table 5.1 ArrayList properties and methods

Here's some example code using ArrayLists:

```
System.Collections.ArrayList arrayOfItems =
            new System.Collections.ArrayList();

arrayOfItems.Add(10);                  // add an integer to the list
arrayOfItems.Add(3.141);               // add a double to the list
arrayOfItems.Add("string");        // add a string to the same list
int listCount = arrayOfItems.Count;    // How many items?
arrayOfItems.Remove(3.141);        // remove first occurrence of 3.141
arrayOfItems.RemoveAt(1);          // remove second item now ("string")
arrayOfItems.Insert(0, "I'm first");        // new first item
arrayOfItems[1] = (int)arrayOfItems[1]+1;    // add 1 – note cast to integer

foreach (var i in arrayOfItems)            // display list – only 2 items
  {
    MessageBox.Show(i.ToString()+" is type: " +i.GetType());
  }
arrayOfItems.Clear( );             // Clear the arrayList
```

As can be seen above, 'foreach' is often used to read through an ArrayList.

See the self assessment exercises for more examples.

As well as the ArrayList class, the System.Collection namespace contains other classes that deal with collections of data, including:
- Stack (a last-in, first-out collection),
- Queue (a first-in, first-out collection),
- SortedList (a collection that can be sorted by a key and can be accessed by key or data) and
- HashTable (a sparsely populated collection of data that can be accessed by a key).

5.10 System.Collection.Generic namespace

The .NET framework also includes the System.Collection.Generic namespace which has generic versions of the classes mentioned above. This means that you specify the data type stored in the collection. This provides a check at compile time rather than at run-time. Consequently, there is less coding (by you) to check for run-time errors, no need for casting the objects and there is improved efficiency.

The classes are:

- Dictionary<K, V> An unordered collection of key and value pairs <K, V> that can be accessed by a key.
- LinkedList<T> A list containing a data type <T> where each item points to the previous and next ones. Items can be removed from or added to the lists.
- List<T> A generic ArrayList containing a data type <T>.
- Queue<T> A generic Queue containing a data type <T>.
- SortedDictionary<K, V> A Dictionary with binary-tree sorted values <V>, accessed by key <K>.
- SortedList<K, V> A generic SortedList of values <V>, accessed by key <K>.
- Stack<T> A generic Stack.

The <T> means you have to specify the type, and the <K, V> means you have to specify a Key type and a Value type. Let's explain with a few examples.

Example: List<T>

This creates a list of any data type (<T>). This is has an interface known as ICollection, which basically provides the properties Capacity and Count, as well as the methods we have seen (Add, Clear, Contains, CopyTo, Remove). It also provides methods to search, sort, and manipulate lists.

The following code snippet shows the code for two buttons that add and remove items.

Don't forget you will need using System.Collections.Generic; at the top of your code.

The List is declared with the data type it is to hold:

```
List<int> numberList = new List<int>( );

// Add button code

private void btnAdd_Click(object sender, EventArgs e)
{
  Random randomNumber = new Random( );   // new random number
  int rndNo = randomNumber.Next(10);     // number from 0 to 9

  // Add the number to the list
  numberList.Add(rndNo);

  // display the list items
  string strItems = string.Empty;
  for (int i=0; i<numberList.Count; i++)
  {
    strItems += "random number " + numberList[i].ToString() +
```

```
            " is position " + i.ToString()+"\r\n";
        }
    MessageBox.Show(strItems);
}


// Remove button code

private void btnRemove_Click(object sender, EventArgs e)
{
    Random randomNumber = new Random( );    // new random number

    // remove a random item from the list
    if (numberList.Count > 1)
            numberList.RemoveAt(randomNumber.Next(numberList.Count));

    // display the list items
    string strItems = string.Empty;
    for (int i = 0; i < numberList.Count; i++)
    {
        strItems += "random number " + numberList[i].ToString() +
                    " is position " + i.ToString()+"\r\n";
    }
    MessageBox.Show(strItems);
}
```

Note that if you try to add a non-integer value as follows, a compile-time error occurs.

```
    numberList.Add("string");   // will error
```

Example - Dictionary

A Dictionary holds two linked types, they are a unique key <K>, used to lookup the table and a corresponding value <V>. For instance a Dictionary could hold two strings: a word and its definition, synonym, antonym or foreign language equivalent. It could hold an integer and a double, say for a lookup table. In the following example it's a stock list with the key the item in stock (a fruit) and the value the number in stock.

The advantages of using a Dictionary over a 2D array are that they can be manipulated, added to, removed, sorted etc.

The key and the value is also a data structure, called a KeyValuePair.

Firstly, don't forget to add using system.collections.generic; at the top of the code. The dictionary is declared using the code:

```
    Dictionary<string, int> myStock = new Dictionary<string, int>( );
```

Note the data types are declared between the '<' and '>' brackets, and the '( )' brackets are also used.

The key is a string containing the fruit, and the value is the amount in stock.

Items are initially added using the code:

```
myStock.Add("apples",1);
myStock.Add("oranges", 2);
myStock.Add("bananas", 3);
```

The new fruits (the keys) will automatically be created. If a key already exists, it's an error.

Once added to the dictionary, the value can be read using:

```
int stockValue = myStock["oranges"] ;
```

The value can be incremented or changed using:

```
myStock["apples"]++;      // increment stock
myStock["oranges"] = 4;   // four in stock now
```

To take an item from stock the value is decremented using:

```
myStock["apples"] = myStock["apples"] -1;      // or
myStock["apples"] --;       // (minus,minus) decrement stock
```

Items can be removed from stock completely using the code:

```
myStock.Remove("bananas");
```

New items can also be added using the key as follows:

```
// If a key does not exist, a new key/value pair is added.
myStock["pineapple"] = 12;
```

The easiest way to access the dictionary (stock) is to use the foreach code:

```
foreach (KeyValuePair<string, int> kvPair in myStock)
{
    MessageBox.Show("Key = " + kvPair.Key + " Value = " + kvPair.Value);
}
```

The Keys and values can be displayed as follows:

```
// display keys - using foreach
foreach (string s in myStock.Keys)          // myStock.Keys is a string
{
    MessageBox.Show("Keys = " + s);
}

// display values - using foreach
foreach (int i in myStock.Values)            // myStock.Values is an int
{
    MessageBox.Show("Values = " + i);
}
```

You can't find the keys using code such as 'myStock.Keys[0]', you have to copy them to a List of myStock.Keys as follows:

```
List<string> keys = new List<string>(myStock.Keys);    // keys are a string
// keys are now in the list keys[i]
// display them and their values
for (int i = 0; i < keys.Count; i++)
{
    MessageBox.Show("Key is " + keys[i].ToString() +
            ", Value is " + myStock[keys[i]].ToString());
}
```

Finally items can be removed and the dictionary checked if it contains a key as follows:

```
// remove the bananas from stock
myStock.Remove("bananas");

// see if they are still there using 'ContainsKey'
if (myStock.ContainsKey("bananas"))
    MessageBox.Show("Banana stock is " + myStock["bananas"].ToString());
else
    MessageBox.Show("Yes, we have no bananas");
```

5.11 Self Assessment Exercises

1. Declare an array of 5 double values and then instantiate it using:

```
double[ ] myDblArray;
myDblArray = new double[5];
```

Write a program to fill the array with data in a 'for' loop using the .Length property.

2. Declare a string array and fill it with data in one statement using:

```
string[] myStrArray = { "str1", "str2", "str3", "str4", "str5" };
```

Write a program to display the values using a 'for' loop, then using a foreach loop (see next chapter)

3. Declare a multidimensional array of students' scores for 5 students and 3 scores.
   Hint: example code 3 students and 2 scores:

```
double [ , ] score;            // declare 2D array of double
score = new double[3,2];       // set size
```

or you can use:
```
twoDArray = new double[3, 2] { { 12, 13.1 }, { 22.1, 33.1 }, { 44.1, 55.5 } };
```

Fill the table for scores 1 and 2 for each student, and calculate the third score as 60% score1 + 40% score2.

Extend the program to display the total score (score3).

See if you can use the array method 'Average' to display the average mark.

4. Structures - 1
You might find this useful to do as we start on object oriented programming.

Create a new Windows application called Structures and place a button on the form. Declare the structure and add the button click code, so that the complete code is as follows:

```
namespace Structures
{
    public partial class Form1 : Form
    {
        struct personnelRecord
        {
            public string name;
            public int age;
            public double salary;
            public char gender;
            public personnelRecord(string name, int age, double salary, char gender)
            {
                this.name = name;
                this.age = age;
                this.salary = salary;
                this.gender = gender;
            }
```

```
    } // end declaration of struct

    private void button1_Click(object sender, EventArgs e)
    {
      personnelRecord[] PersonnelList = new personnelRecord[10];
      PersonnelList[0].name = "Freda Bloggs";
      PersonnelList[1].age = 21;
      PersonnelList[5].salary = 20000;
      PersonnelList[9].gender = 'F';
      MessageBox.Show("Name is "+PersonnelList[0].name+
        "\n\rage is "+PersonnelList[1].age+
        "\n\rsalary is "+PersonnelList[5].salary+
        "\n\rgender is "+PersonnelList[9].gender);
    } // end button click

  }
}
```

Modify this code so that the information for each person is requested and then displayed.

Structures - 2
Create a structure for a car dealership with 3 items, Car Name (string), Car mileage (int) and Price (float).

Create an array of 5 cars and set the name, mileage and price for some of the cars.

Display all the car's information on a button click, using messageBox.Show( );

5. Strings

Declare a string called 'str29Chars' and set it to: "This string has 29 characters".
Display the length of the string using the .Length property.

5.1 Use the substring method to display the first eleven characters in the string, e.g:
```
      MessageBox.Show(("Mary had a little lamb").Substring(0,4));
          // displays 'Mary'
```

5.2 Determine the starting index of the number 29 using the IndexOf( ) method, e.g:
```
  MessageBox.Show(("Mary had a lamb").IndexOf("ry ha").ToString( ));
          // displays 2
```

5.3 Declare a new string 'str33', copy the 'str29Chars' string to it and replace the number 29 with 33 in 'str33' using the Replace( ) method, e.g:
```
      string strMaryText = "Mary had a little lamb";
      string strReplacedText = strMaryText.Replace("lamb", "sheep");
```

5.4 Use the .CompareTo( ) method to compare the strings 'str33' and 'str29Chars'and note the value that is returned.

6. Dynamic arrays using Arraylist

To show how we declare, add and clear and ArrayList, try this exercise which randomly adds an integer, a floating point number or a string to an ArrayList and copies this to a listbox.

Start a new project and add a ListBox and two buttons on the form, Change the Text for button 1 to 'Add item' and for button 2 to 'Clear'. see figure 5.3.

Figure 5.3 ArrayList example

The complete code to declare the ArrayList and for the button clicks is as follows:

```csharp
public partial class Form1 : Form
{
    public Form1()
    {
        InitializeComponent();
    }

    private System.Collections.ArrayList arrayOfItems
            = new System.Collections.ArrayList( );

    private void button2_Click(object sender, EventArgs e)
    {
        arrayOfItems.Clear();
    }

    private void button1_Click(object sender, EventArgs e)
```

```
{
    Random randomNumber = new Random();        // new random number
    int rndNo = randomNumber.Next(3);          // number from 0 to 2

  switch (rndNo)                               // get random item to add
  {
      case 0: arrayOfItems.Add(randomNumber.Next(10));       // add integer
          break;
      case 1: arrayOfItems.Add(randomNumber.Next(10)*Math.PI); // add f.p
          break;
      case 2: arrayOfItems.Add("string");                    // add string
          break;
  }

  listBox1.Items.Clear( );                     // clear listbox of old items

  for (int i = 0; i < arrayOfItems.Count; i++)
  {
      listBox1.Items.Add(arrayOfItems[i]);     // add items to the listbox
  }
 }
 }
}
```

7. Using a Dictionary

Create a stock inventory using a Dictionary. Place a list box containing stock items (e.g. fruit) and add buttons and code to increment and decrement stock by choosing items from the list box. Add a button to remove an item completely and also to add a new item to the list box and the stock. Use a List to display all the keys in the Dictionary.

5.12 Summary

This has been a very detailed chapter on the language and used some items (such as foreach) that we will cover later. Feel free to return to read the parts you want and return to this when you need.

We have looked at arrays, and seen how we declare and use single and multi-dimensional arrays. We have seen how to declare a structure, an array that contains different data types, which will lead us into object oriented code later. We have seen character arrays and strings, and some of the many string handling operations have been seen.

We have seen some advanced data handling techniques in creating dynamic arrays with the ArrayList object, and some of the generic Collections items such as List and Dictionary.

Chapter 6 - Program Flow, Loops and Decisions

6.1 Introduction

Sooner or later your program will need to make a decision and alter its course. There are five basic ways a C# program controls the flow of the program, they are:

- if .. else
- switch .. case
- for and foreach
- while
- do while

We shall look at each of these in turn and also look at exception handling.

6.2 The if statement

The simplest decision making construct is the 'if' statement. It takes the form of:

```
if ( condition )
{
   statement(s)
}
```

The condition is a logical comparison which produces a true or false (a Boolean) answer. The condition must be enclosed in brackets. For example:

```
if ( bankBalance > 1000000 )
{
   MessageBox.Show ("I'm a millionaire");
}
```

If there is only one statement (as above) it doesn't need to be in curly brackets, but if there is more than one statement they must be enclosed in curly brackets, so it's good practice to use them anyway.

The logical comparisons take the following forms:

Operator	English	Example
==	is equal to	(2+2) == 4
!=	is not equal to	(1+2) != 4
<	is less than	X < 2
<=	is less than or equal to	Y <= 3
>	is greater than	X > Y
>=	is greater than or equal to	(X+Y) >= Z

The test does not have to be a simple one; it can test complicated expressions so long as there is a true or false result.

6.2.1 The if .. else statement

The 'if' statement can be extended to add an else clause. This is the if .. else, which takes the form of:

```
if ( condition )
{
  statements1
}
else
{
  statements2
}
```

Here statements1 are executed if the condition is true, and statements2 are executed if the condition is false. For example:

```
if ( expenditure > income )
{
  MessageBox.Show ("Miserable");      // if expenditure > income
}
else
{
  MessageBox.Show ("Happy");          // if expenditure =< income
}
```

You can have multiple statements (contained within curly brackets) for either of the statements.

Additional if .. else statements can be included within other if .. else statements. However you can still have only one ending else statement, e.g.:

```
if ( condition )
{
  statement(s)
}
else if ( condition )
{
  statement(s)
}
else if ( condition )
{
  statement(s)
```

```
     }
     . .
     // more of the same
     else
     {
       end statement
     }
```

6.2.2 The if .. else shortcut

You can use, or may see, the question mark and colon shortcut for if else: '? :'
For example the code:

```
if (x != 0.0)
    s = Math.Sin(x)/x;
else
    s = 1.0;
```

becomes:

```
s = x != 0.0 ? Math.Sin(x)/x : 1.0;
```

I'll let you decide which is more readable.

6.3 The switch statement

There may come a time when there you have multiple if or if.. else statements, e.g.

```
If (age == 12) { MessageBox.Show ("you are nearly a teenager") ; }
If (age == 13) { MessageBox.Show ("you are a teenager") ; }
If (age == 18) { MessageBox.Show ("you can vote") ; }
If (age == 20) { MessageBox.Show ("you are no longer a teenager") ; }
If (age == 21) { MessageBox.Show ("you're an adult – congratulations") ; }
```

The switch statement makes programming this slightly easier and more readable. The format is:

```
switch ( expression )
{
case statements
default statement
}
```

The expression must be an integer or a string which evaluates to one of the case statements. The statement(s) that match the case are executed. If there is no match, the default statement is executed, but you don't have to have a default statement block.

The code above would become:

```
switch ( age )
{
  case 12 :
  {
    MessageBox.Show ("You are nearly a teenager ") ;
    break ;
  }
  case 13 :
  {
    MessageBox.Show ("You are a teenager") ;
    break ;
  }
  case 18 :
  {
    MessageBox.Show ("You can vote") ;
    break ;
  }
  case 20 :
  {
    MessageBox.Show ("You are no longer a teenager") ;
    break ;
  }
  case 21 :
  {
    MessageBox.Show ("You're an adult – congratulations") ;
    break;
  }
  default :
  {
    MessageBox.Show ("You are not 12, 13, 18, 20 or 21.") ;
    break ;
  }
}
```

Note the **break** statement. The break ends the **case** statement. C# does not support an implicit fall through from one case label to the next and you will get an error if the case statements do not end with a **break** or a **goto** statement. The one exception is if a **case** statement has no code. For example, you can have:

```
case 6:              // no code  – will go to next case
case 7:              // no code  – will go to next case
case 8: MessageBox.Show ("executed for values of 6, 7, or 8"); break;
```

You can't have more than one condition in a case. You can't have the following:

```
case 6, 7, 8 : MessageBox.Show ("You are 6, 7, or 8") ;
        // This will error
```

You can however use the goto statement to change the flow. For instance you could have:

```
case 6:
  {
    MessageBox.Show ("You are 6");
    goto case 8;
  }
case 7:
  {
    MessageBox.Show ("You are 7");
    goto case 8;
  }
case 8:
  {
    MessageBox.Show ("executed for values of 6, 7, or 8");
    break;
  }
```

6.3.1 The goto statement

You may be surprised to see the goto statement. C# allows a goto jump to a labelled statement, but the label must be within the scope of the jump. This means you can jump out of a statement block, class or 'finally' block. However the use of goto is frowned upon as it contravenes good programming practice and makes programs difficult to understand and document.

6.3.2 Switching on a string variable

As stated earlier, you can also switch on a string variable, for example:

```
switch ( textBox1.Text )
{
  case "cut": MessageBox.Show ("cut"); break;
  case "copy": MessageBox.Show ("copy"); break;
  case "paste": MessageBox.Show("paste"); break;
}
```

6.4 Looping - The for statement

The for loop statement is used when you know the start and finish points of the loop. The construct is:

```
for (variable = start expression ; end condition ; increment expression )
  {
    statement(s)
  }
```

The first statement is executed once only at the beginning of the loop and is normally an initialization statement (e.g. int i = 1;). The end condition determines when the loop terminates. This is evaluated at the beginning of each loop. Finally, the increment (or decrement) expression is executed each iteration of the loop. If the increment expression is an empty statement (a semicolon by itself) the loop will never terminate. You can use the break statement to terminate the loop early.

Example: Initializing an array

Suppose you wish to clear an array: a loop will easily do it. The loop code is

```
for (int count = 0 ; count <10 ; count++)
  {
    intArray [count] = 0;
  }
```

This declares and sets the loop variable 'count' to 0. The end condition (count < 10) is performed, and count is incremented by one each time around the loop (count ++). This continues until count reaches the value 10. The loop will be executed ten times with values for count from 0 to 9.

You can change the loop variable by a value other than one if you change 'count++' to say 'count=count+3, or 'count=count-5'. Note that the increment/decrement expression does NOT end with a semicolon, and the editor will highlight this as an error.

If the loop variable is declared within the loop as above (int count =0) it only exists within the loop.

The editor automatically indents the code which helps to show the content of a loop. It is also a good idea to add a comment at the end of loops (e.g. // end of count loop). As mentioned you can use the break statement to finish the loop early.

Loops are often used to count through the elements in an array, or the characters in a string.

Points to note:

- The loop variable can only be an integer.
- The loop variable is initialized in the for loop; you don't have to initialize it beforehand.

- The loop variable can start with any integer number.
- You should not alter the loop variable within the loop.
- The terminal value does not have to be a number; it can be a variable, say N, as long as it is defined before entering the loop.
- The loop variable may be decremented rather than incremented by using count-- or count=count-n as the increment expression.

See the self assessment exercises for more examples

6.4.1 The foreach statement

C# also provides a 'foreach' loop. This provides a simple way to iterate through all the elements of an array or collection of objects such as a List. You do not have to specify an end condition or an increment. The following example creates an array called numbers and iterates through it with the foreach statement:

```
int[ ] numbers = { 4, 1, 6, -5, 3, 2, -2, 1, 0 };

foreach (int i in numbers)
{
    MessageBox.Show (i.ToString( ));
}
```

When this program runs it displays the values in the array, (4, 1, 6 etc.) not the value of i. This should be used for reading arrays and object data only, not setting values.

We saw this in the chapter on arrays and collections and you might like to revisit that example.

6.5 The while and do-while statements.

The while or do-while loops are used when the loop variable has to be changed by a varying amount, or a test occurs within the loop.

The while loop

The format of the while loop is:

```
while (expression)
{
    statement(s)
}
```

The expression is evaluated at the beginning of the loop, and the statements are executed while the expression is true.

The **do-while** loop

This is similar to the while loop except that the expression is evaluated at the end of the loop:

```
do
{
   statement(s)
}
while (expression);                        // Note the semicolon
```

The do-while is convenient to use when the statements within the loop must be executed at least once. For example, when reading information from a file, keyboard or some input, you know that you will always read at least one character:

Exercise: The Fibonacci series.

The Fibonacci series occurs widely in nature and is the sum of the previous two numbers in the series starting with 0 and 1: 0, 1, 1, 2, 3, 5, 8, 13, 21 etc. The ratio of the last two numbers approaches the golden ratio (1.61803399), for example $21/13 = 1.615$.

The following code displays the Fibonacci series whilst the sum is less than 10.

Place a button on a form and give it the caption: 'Fibonacci Series'
Add a list box to display the series.
Add the following code for the button:

```
private void button1_Click(object sender, EventArgs e)
{
  int old, next, sum;
  old=0;
  next=1;
  sum = old+next;
  while (sum <10)
  {
    sum=old + next;
    listBox1.Items.Add (old+" plus "+next+" is "+sum);
    old=next;
    next= sum;
  } // end of while sum<10
}
```

Run the program to display the first few numbers of the Fibonacci Series, see figure 6.1.

Figure 6.1 Fibonacci series

Exercise: Modify the code to show more numbers in the sequence.

You might like to try the do.. while version:

```
int old, next, sum;
old=0;
next=1;
sum = old+next;
do
{
  sum = old + next;
  listBox1.Items.Add(old + " plus " + next + " is " + sum);
  old = next;
  next = sum;
}
while (sum < 10);     // end of do .. while sum<10
```

6.6 Exceptions. The try-catch code

Your programs may error at run-time. These are known as exceptions. For instance, exceptions can happen on something as simple as a divide by zero, converting a blank textbox field into a number, or opening a file that doesn't exist or is already in use by another application. The operating system will trap exceptions and display a message, but your program should really deal with your exceptions and display relevant messages to your user.

C# provides 'try' and 'catch' code (along with 'throw' and 'finally') to deal with exceptions, trapping them out and allowing your code to deal with the exceptions. Your program can 'try' a section of code and if any exceptions occur, deal with them in the 'catch' code.

Let's see how we can trap a divide by zero error.

Exercise: Try and catch code

Start a new project and add a button to the form. Add the follow exception code to the button click:

```
int number1=123, zero = 0;
try
{
    number1 = number1 / zero;     // will error
}
catch (DivideByZeroException)
{
    MessageBox.Show("You divided by zero!");
}
```

You can leave out the 'DivideByZeroException' part of the catch statement, in which case all exceptions will be trapped. There are lots of different types of exceptions. To view them all, type any letter after the opening bracket for the catch and the IntelliSense will display them, see figure 6.2.

Figure 6.2 Catch exceptions

For instance, the numbers to be divided might have been read from a text box. To ensure a valid number has been entered into the text box, you could check for a FormatException as well as the DivideByZeroException as follows:

```
try
{
    int number1 = Convert.ToInt32(textBox1.Text);
    int number2 = Convert.ToInt32(textBox2.Text);
    textBox3.Text = (number1 / number2).ToString();
}
catch (FormatException)
{
    MessageBox.Show("Please check your numbers");
}
```

```
    catch (DivideByZeroException)
    {
        MessageBox.Show("You divided by zero!");
    }
}
```

There are two extensions to the try-catch code. They are throw and finally. The throw statement passes the exception to the calling method and the finally statements are always executed and can be used to tidy up.

6.7 Self Assessment Exercises

1. Watch the supporting videos pointed to at Elektor's web site.

2. If exercise
Write if statements that use all of the comparison operators (==, <=, >=, etc.)
Extend this to include multiple comparisons and test your programs. For example, test for:
if integerA is greater than integerB and integerC is less than integerD, and test for:
if integerA is less than integerB or integerC is greater than integerD.

3. If then else exercise.
Write a program that requests an income value and determines the Tax due to the Government, if its tax system is as follows:
    Income:
    £0-1999: 0%,
    £2k-2999: 10%,
    £3k-39999: 22%,
    Over 40k: 40%.

4. Switch exercise
Remove the default statement and complete the switch statement in section 6.3 so that a message is displayed for every teenage year. Combine years 14 to 17 so that the program drops through years 14 to 16 and displays a message for year 17: "You are between 14 and 17".

5. 'for' loop exercises:

Exercise: Two times table.

Start a new project and place a list box on a form.
Add a button and change its Caption property to 'Two Times Table'. Add the following code for the button click and run the code:

```
private void button1_Click(object sender, EventArgs e)
{
```

```
for (int count = 1; count <= 12; count++)
{
  listBox1.Items.Add(count+" times 2 is "+count*2);
}          // end of for loop
}
```

Your output should be similar to the following figure:

```
1 times 2 is 2
2 times 2 is 4
3 times 2 is 6
4 times 2 is 8
5 times 2 is 10
6 times 2 is 12
7 times 2 is 14
8 times 2 is 16
9 times 2 is 18
10 times 2 is 20
11 times 2 is 22
12 times 2 is 24
```

More times tables
Display the three times table, starting at 1 x 3 going up to 12 x 3.
Display the four times table, starting at 12 x 4 going down to 0 x 4.

6. While loop
Declare and set an integer to zero.
Use a while loop to loop while the integer is less than 3, displaying the value in a message box. Increment the integer in the loop.

7. Do-while loop
Declare and set an integer to three.
In a do-while loop, display the integer value in a message box while the integer is more than zero. Decrement the integer in the loop.

8. Replace the code in section 5.9 that checks for a stock item (copied below), with try and catch code

```
if (myStock.ContainsKey("bananas"))
  MessageBox.Show("Banana stock is " + myStock["bananas"].ToString());
else
  MessageBox.Show("Yes, we have no bananas");
```

6.8 Summary

This chapter has covered different ways of changing program flow and looping. These are the commands:

- if .. else
- switch .. case
- the for loop
- while
- do .. while loops.

These statements use a test (a comparison) that provides a true or false result to determine the program code to execute.

The 'for' loop is used when the loop conditions are known. The while and do .. while statements are used when the loop variable has to be changed by a varying amount, or a test occurs within the loop. The while loop tests at the beginning of the code, whilst the do .. while statement tests at the end of the code statements.

Finally we considered exception handling code using the try-catch, throw and finally statements.

Chapter 7 - Object oriented programming: Methods and classes

7.1 Introduction

By now you may have realised that the programs written so far have been broken up into small portions of code, such as a button click or a timer tick event. We have used other code which we haven't written such as MessageBox.Show. Modules of code like these are called methods.

It is good practice to break your program into small parts which have a specific function and consequently are easier to get debugged and working. These smaller methods can be used in other programs, in turn making those quicker and easier to write. If you look again at the code to display the List items in chapter 5.9, you can see that it is duplicated. This could have been written as a method, saving memory space and possible errors.

If you have programmed in other languages you might call these functions, procedures or subroutines.

When we deal with object oriented code later we shall introduce classes, which are a combination of data and methods. We have already seen the DateTime and Math classes and their methods (e.g. AddDays( ) and Sqrt( )).

By convention, method and class names begin with a capital letter, whereas variables begin with a lower case letter. Hence just by looking at the name you can tell if it's a method or a variable. You should use this scheme for your names.

7.2 Method declaration

Let's see how we write a method and use it in our program. Methods may have data passed to them and returned from them.

A method declaration starts with the data type of the value returned or the keyword 'void' if none. It is followed by the method's name and then a list of parameters passed in brackets (their data types and name to be used in the method). The method's own data and code is encased in a block within curly brackets:

> *return-data-type   Method-name   (parameter-list in brackets)*
> *{*
> *   // Method declarations and statements*
> *}*

As an example, let's see how we would define an integer square root method. We will pass an integer and return a double value.

The declaration starts with the return data type (double) followed by the method name (SquareRoot) and then the data type of the parameters passed and a name that will be used inside the method. If there is more than one parameter, each is separated by a comma and needs its own data type.

The method's code is:

```
double SquareRoot ( int intRoot)
{
  double root = Math.Sqrt(intRoot);
  return root ;                        // squareRoot returns a double
}
```

Note that the integer value that is passed is called 'intRoot' in the method but may have another name in the calling program. The return keyword followed by the variable's name must be used to state which variable is to be passed back to the calling program.

If nothing is returned the keyword 'void' is used for the return data type in the method declaration,and of course no 'return' statement is needed. If nothing is passed to the method, the brackets are still needed but left empty.

The method cannot be placed inside a method, and is placed at the same level as a button click.

To run (or call) the method from the main program, we use the method's name followed by the parameters we want to pass to it. In this case, as the method returns a value, the result will need to be assigned somewhere so it is placed after an equals sign, e.g.:

```
double dblSqRoot = SquareRoot ( integerNumber ) ;
```

You do not have to state the data type of the parameters passed when the method is called; that will have been declared before the call is made.

You can of course declare variables to be used within the method.

Exercise: A Simple method

Let's try an example before we go any further. We'll start with a method that doesn't accept or return any values. Although this may seem an odd thing to do, it might be useful if you want a method to initialize some values or reset all the controls on a form. We'll create a method that just waits for a short time.

Start a new windows application; call it 'Wait'. Place a button on the form and give it a suitable name (I've used btnWait). Double-click the button and change the code to be:

```
private void btnWait_Click(object sender, EventArgs e)
{
    Wait( );
```

```
   }
```

To declare the Wait method, place the following code before the button click method:

```
void Wait( )
{
    int i = 0;
    while (i < 10)
      {
        i = i + 1;
      }
}
```

Remember that even though nothing is returned, we have to state that fact using the word 'void' in the method declaration.

Run the program and click the button to call the method. Of course your computer won't wait for very long.

7.3 Parameter passing

We will want to pass data to and from our methods. For our example, we may want to wait for different amounts of time or pass a message back when it's done waiting.

Let's look at all the possibilities. We can:

1. Pass nothing, return nothing,
2. Pass something, return nothing,
3. Pass nothing, return something,
4. Pass something, return something.

The first case we have just seen. Take another look at the method declaration now 'void Wait( );' and see how the method is called using its name: Wait( );

Let's look at the second case and pass a variable which will be an integer value that will be used as a delay time.

Declare a new method called PassWaitingTime as follows. Add this before your 'void Wait( )' line of code.

```
void PassWaitingTime(int delayTime)
{
    int  i = 0;
    while (i < delayTime)
    {
        i = i + 1;
```

```
        }
    }
```

This method is passed an integer which is called delayTime within the method.

To call the method, add the following code after the Wait( ); in the button click code:

```
        PassWaitingTime(100);
```

Run the code. It should wait a bit longer this time – but of course you still won't notice it.

This isn't much use if we can only pass the value of 100 each time and of course we can pass a variable.

Change the PassWaitingTime(100); to the following:

```
        int longTime = 10000;
        int shortTime = 10;
        PassWaitingTime(longTime);
        PassWaitingTime(shortTime);
```

Run the code again. This time it waits 10000 loops followed by 10 loops. You still won't notice the delay.

Note the variable name is longTime or shortTime in main program, but always called delayTime in method. You can declare a variable called delayTime in the button click, but it is different from the one in the Wait method.

What if we want to pass nothing, but returning a value? Let's look at our first Wait( ) method but now return a string "done" when it's finished. As this method is going to return a string, the word 'void' will be replaced by 'string' in the method's declaration. We will also have to do something with the string that is returned.

Add this method code before the void PassWaitingTime(int delayTime) code:

```
        string ReturnWait( )
        {
            int i = 0;
            while (i < 10)
            {
                i = i + 1;
            }
            return "done";
        }
```

In our main program, let's display the string it returns. Add the following code after the Wait(shortTime); line of code in the button click:

```
MessageBox.Show(ReturnWait( ));
```

Run the code. The MessageBox.Show method will call ReturnWait and display 'done' when the waiting is over.

Finally let's pass a variable and return a value:

Add a new method PassReturnWait. (I'll let you think about where to put this)

```
string PassReturnWait(int delayTime)
{
   int i = 0;
   while (i < delayTime)
   {
      i = i + 1;
   }
   return "done";
}
```

And add the following code in the button click method:

```
shortTime = 10;
MessageBox.Show(PassReturnWait( shortTime));
```

Check that it works.

We may want to pass or return more than one value. We can pass many variables, but generally only return one. Parameters are passed as a list between the brackets and we've seen an example of this in the button click method itself:

```
private void button1_Click(object sender, EventArgs e)
```

Here the object (the button) and the type of event (a mouse click mouseEvent) are passed to the method. You can test for this in the button click code, but more of that later.

7.4 Pass by reference - ref and out keywords.

In the examples we have seen, a copy of the parameter is passed to the method and the original remains intact. This is known as pass by value. However, it is possible to let the method access and permanently change the value. This is known as 'pass by reference'. In this case the keyword 'ref' is used. The keyword 'out' is also used for methods that also initialize and return the variable.

If we return to our original square root example and change it to pass by reference, it becomes:

```
double SquareRoot (ref int intRoot)
{
  // code goes here
  // no return statement needed
}
```

Now neither a return statement nor an assignment statement in the main code is needed.

This becomes important if we pass an array element or a whole array to a method. An array element is passed by value, for example if we have a method called 'Modify':

```
public void Modify (int  intModify)
{
  intModify  = intModify *2;
}
```

which is called by the code:

```
int [ ] intArray = { 1, 2, 3, 4, 5, 6 };
Modify (intArray[3]);
```

This does not change the original value in the array, as it was passed by value.

However, if we have a method that squares an array:

```
public void SquareArray(int[] anArray)
{
  for (int j = 0; j < anArray.Length; j++)
  {
    anArray[j] = anArray[j] * anArray[j];
  }
}
```

which is called using:

```
int[] intArray = { 1, 2, 3, 4, 5, 6 };
SquareArray(intArray);
```

The whole array is passed by reference and squared, even though the ref keyword isn't used.

7.5 Scope of a method - private and public.

As we have seen with variables, the block of code to which they are available is known as the scope. Eventually your programs will consist of many methods and classes and you will need to consider their scope. The main scope are private and public; **private** is the least permissive access level and items are accessible only within the body of the class in which they are declared; **public** is the most permissive access level, with no restrictions their access.

We shall see some other modifiers such as 'static' and 'protected' later.

7.6 Recursion

Recursive methods are ones that call themselves. This can't go on forever of course and so there must be a way of eventually stopping the recursive call and if necessary return a value.

Consider a method that works out the factorial of a number. The factorial of a number, N, is the multiplication of all the numbers up that number. It is denoted by N! and defined for N>0 as N! = N x (N-1)! where 0! =1.

For example the factorial of 4 is 4*3*2*1*0

4! = 4*3! = 4*3*2! = 4*3*2*1! = 4*3*2*1*0!! = 4*3*2*1*1.

A recursive method can then be defined which calls itself with a number one less than the number passed until the number is one. A method that performs this is shown below.

```
int Factorial(int factorialNo)
{
    if (factorialNo == 0)
    {
        return 1;
    }
    else
    {
        return factorialNo = factorialNo * Factorial(factorialNo - 1);
    }
}
```

The method is passed and returns an integer. The second return statement calls the Factorial method itself with the number one less than the one passed. This continues until the number 0 is passed, when the value 1 is returned. The calls then undo themselves calculating the required value.

7.7 Calling an event

As we have seen events such as a button click are written as a method, and your program can call these methods and hence cause an event to occur, e.g. to force a button click. The correct parameters need to be passed to the method of course.

Let's take an example. Place two buttons and a text box on a form and write the following code for the button clicks.

Now clicking button1, writes 'Hi there' into the text box. Clicking button2 calls the button1 click event to perform the same action. Note that the button click event expects an object and EventArgs data types to be passed to it (object sender, EventArgs e). You must pass (null, e) or (sender, e) to it in this case.

```
private void button1_Click(object sender, EventArgs e)
{
    textBox1.Text = "Hi there";
}

private void button2_Click(object sender, EventArgs e)
{
    button1_Click(null, e);
}
```

7.8 Classes and Namespaces

We shall see in the next chapter that a class contains both data and methods to manipulate that data and is a template for an object. A namespace is a collection of classes and their methods.

The .NET library is composed of many namespaces. We have seen some of them such as System, System.IO, System.Windows.Forms. They are included in our program with the 'using' keyword. Namespaces are stored in dynamic link locate (DLL) files called assemblies. We shall see how to create our own DLL program and include them in our own libraries in chapter 18.

7.9 Self Assessment Exercises

1. Watch the supporting videos pointed to at Elektor's web site.

2. Place some text boxes on a form, and write a method that clears the text in the boxes. This method isn't passed or returns any data. Call this method from a button click and try it out.

3. Create a method that when called rolls a die (a single dice) and returns the number displayed. It's not passed anything but returns an integer value from 1 to 6.

4. Write a method that rolls a number of dice. It is passed the number of dice to roll and returns the total number thrown.

5. Write a method that rolls up to three dice. It is passed the number of dice to roll and returns a number 1 to 6 for each of the dice rolled and zero for the dice not rolled. You will have to pass four parameters and either use the out or ref keyword or pass an array.

6. Create a method that rolls a number of dice and returns the values. This time pass one variable - an array. The first value in the array holds the number of dice to roll and the rest of the array returns the dice values. In this case the array will be passed by reference, i.e. the whole array is passed (or more accurately the address of the array is passed). See the array examples in section 7.4 to see how a whole array is passed to a method.

7. Try writing a similar method that passes one array value only. See if the value is changed in the calling program. It shouldn't be. If you want it to be changed pass the value with the ref keyword and prove it.

8. Write a program that requests a number and calculates its factorial using recursive calls. Change the method so that it deals with long integer data types and large factorials.

7.10 Summary

This chapter has looked at breaking your program down into smaller more manageable parts called methods. We have seen how to declare a method and how to pass data to the method from our program and how to return values from method using the return keyword.

We have seen how to pass array elements and whole arrays to a method and discussed the ref and out keywords.

We have discussed private and public methods and recursion and also seen how we can call our events, which are methods themselves.

Chapter 8 - Object oriented programming - creating objects

8.1 Introduction

We have covered a lot of programming concepts so far, so now is a good time to look at Object Oriented Programming (OOP). It may seem a little early to talk about this subject so if you want to, skip this and come back, but it does fit in well with the ideas we've been covering and may actually make your programming easier.

First of all, don't panic. Object Oriented Programming was devised to relate computer programs more closely to real items such as a person, car or house and simplify complex applications. We have seen some objects already: the button and the form are objects. We have seen that these objects have methods, properties and events. In this chapter we will see how to create our own objects.

I do not intend to cover OOP in great detail, but simply to give you an idea of what they are and how to use OOP and to create your own objects and use them.

Firstly, let's deal with some terminology.

Class
A class contains both data and methods to manipulate that data and is a template for an object. The code and its data are integrated (or in OOP terms, *encapsulated*). The data can only be manipulated by the class code and this obviously leads to more structured and reliable code. It is from the class that we instantiate (create) our objects using the 'new' keyword that we have seen and used. Objects created in this way are different from each other.

Object
An object is a specific instance (or creation) of a class, created using the 'new' keyword. You have created buttons, which are instances of class Button, and in their own right are different from each other. An object normally has its own data which can only be changed using the object's own interfaces – its methods, properties and events.

Properties
You should be happy with properties by now. We have seen that our controls have properties and how we access the properties using the dot notation. In this chapter we will create an object with methods and properties and be able to access them with the dot notation.

Methods
We discussed methods in the previous chapter. In OOP terms you can think of a method as an action that an object can perform. In a Transport example it might be start, drive, stop, reverse etc. We call an object's method using the dot notation and if necessary pass data to the method in brackets, e.g. MessageBox.Show("message");

8.2 Creating Objects

Let's start creating our own objects. We'll create a simple object, a Point. It will have properties: X and Y. We start by writing a class which has X and Y variables and then instantiate our own Point objects based on this class. We will be able to set and read the X and Y values as properties. We'll add a Move method that will move the point. Later we'll extend this point to a new class called Circle by extending Point and adding a further property, radius.

Exercise: Our first object

Start a new Windows project and call it OOP1. Now add a new class using Project > Add Class or Project > Add New Item > Class. Give it the name Point, see figure 8.1

Figure 8.1 Adding a Class

If you forget to change its name, a class called Class1 will be created. You can delete this by selecting it in the solution explorer and choosing delete.

A new tab entitled Point.cs appears in the design and has the code as follows:

```
namespace OOP1
{
    class Point
    {
    }
}
```

We can now create some new points from the Point class template. Return to the form design and add a button to the form. Change the button click code to the following:

```
private void button1_Click(object sender, EventArgs e)
{
    Point point1;
    point1 = new Point( );
}
```

Notice how the IntelliSense knows about the class Point and variable point1 as you type code, see figures 8.2a and 8.2b.

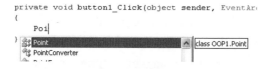

Figure 8.2a IntelliSense display of class

Figure 8.2b IntelliSense display of variable point1

You can also create a new object in one line of code as follows:

```
Point point1 = new Point( );
```

Clicking the button will create new point objects. You have just created your own objects! Of course they don't do anything yet.

Let's add X and Y properties to give a position for the Point. To access them they must be declared public, but to ensure the integrity of the data there must also be internal, private variables; we shall call these _x and _y. The public X and Y properties will be accessed using the dot notation, which will in turn read and write the internal _x and _y values using 'get' and 'set' keyword methods.

Change the Point class code to the following:

```
namespace OOP1
{
    // Point class definition
    class Point
    {
```

```
// private Point coordinates
private int _x, _y;

// constructor - runs when a new Point is instantiated – see later
public Point( )
{
}

// property X
public int X
{
    // allow users to read X property – use lower case for get and set
    get
    {
        return _x;
    }

    // allow users to set X property
    set
    {
        _x = value;
    }
} // end property X

// ditto for property Y
public int Y
{
    get
    {
        return _y;
    }
    set
    {
        _y = value;
    }
} // end property Y

} // end class Point
}
```

Let's explain this before we run the code.

Every Point object you create will have its own private _x and _y values, these are declared with the code private int _x, _y;.

As they are declared private, they can only be accessed within the class, so to allow access using the dot notation, public properties X and Y are declared which access the private values with the get and set code:

```
public int X
{
    get { return _x; }
    set { _x = value; }
} // end property X
```

The get code returns the private _x variable and the set code changes the private _x variable with the value passed. See below for example code that sets and gets values.

Note the variables X and Y have been declared public, and so can be accessed from outside of the class. Once a point has been instantiated, the dot notation code can be used, for example:

```
firstPoint.X = 32;              // set X value
Yposition = firstPoint.Y;       // get Y value
```

To see this in action, change the button code to the following:

```
private void button1_Click(object sender, EventArgs e)
{
    Point firstPoint = new Point( );
    firstPoint.X = 23;
    firstPoint.Y = 345;
    int y = firstPoint.Y;
    MessageBox.Show("X value = " + firstPoint.X.ToString( ) +
        " Y value = " +   y.ToString( ));
}
```

Run the program, the code and output should look like figure 8.3.

```
private void button1_Click(object sender, EventArgs e)
{
    Point firstPoint = new Point( );
    firstPoint.X = 23;
    firstPoint.Y = 345;
    int y = firstPoint.Y;
    MessageBox.Show("X value = " + firstPoint.X.ToString( ) +
        " Y value = " +   y.ToString( ));
}
```

X value = 23 Y value = 345

OK

Figure 8.3 Point Class code and display

Exercise: Add more point objects

Change the button click code so that new Point objects called 'secondPoint' and 'thirdPoint' are created and then set and display their X and Y values.

8.3 Constructors

We may want a way of initializing our objects or to set initial default values, say for X and Y. This is done in the constructor code and an empty constructor was included in the code you typed:

```
// constructor - runs when a new Point is instantiated – see later
    public Point( )
    {
    }
```

The constructor is called whenever a new object is instantiated. If you don't write constructor code a default one is provided. Note the constructor has the same name as the class and even though it has no return value or type, it doesn't include the 'void' keyword.

The constructor code creates a new Point object when the following code is executed:

```
Point firstPoint = new Point( );
```

Remember the 'new' keyword is a way of making a new object from our class which is distinct from all other objects.

Now I hope you understand why we have to write this code when we create a new object and what it does. In this case it just creates the Point – it doesn't have any X or Y values at this time.

We could write code in the constructor to set X and Y to specific values, e.g. set them to zero, as follows:

```
public Point()
{
    _x = 0;
    _y = 0;
}
```

This will set the X and Y values of a new Point to zero. Change your constructor code and prove it.

We may also want constructor code that sets X and Y values points passed when we instantiate the object, i.e. we would write:

```
Point newPoint = new Point(123,456);
```

This will create the object with the properties passed as parameters. Our constructor code won't currently do this, and we will add another constructor and code to do this. This means there will be two constructors.

Before adding the code you might like to think what the second constructor contains. Consider:

   a) Is the constructor code public or private?
   b) What's it called?
   c) What are the parameters passed (what are their type and name)?
   d) What values do we set in the code?

Let's try it. Add the following code after the public Point ( ) constructor:

```
public Point(int xValue, int yValue)
{
    // set x and y
    _x = xValue;
    _y = yValue;
}
```

We have two constructors now, one will be called with if no parameters are used and the other if two parameters (X and Y) are passed. The correct one will be executed depending on the number of parameters used when the object is instantiated. This is one of the features of OOP.

Add the following code for the button click and see it create the new point with the values passed:

```
Point setPoint = new Point(987,654);
MessageBox.Show("X value = " + setPoint.X.ToString( ) +
        " Y value = " +    setPoint.Y.ToString( ));

MessageBox.Show(setPoint.ToString());        // see below
```

Notice that the intelliSense editor knows about both constructors and provides a prompt, see figure 8.4.

```
ιιι σιrυ⊥ιι.r - ɔ4ɔ;
int y = firstPoint.Y;
MessageBox.Show("X value = " + firstPoint.X.ToString( ) +
        " Y value = " +    y.ToString( ));
Point setPoint = new Point(
```
▲ 2 of 2 ▼ Point.Point(**int xValue**, int yValue)

Figure 8.4 Prompt for constructors.

Exercises:

- If you didn't do so, add code in the default constructor so that initial values of X and Y are set to zero.
- Take a look at the code we used when we created our structures in chapter 5.3. You can see that the personnelRecord structure has constructor code and is very similar to our class code.

8.4 The ToString method

Note the setPoint.ToString( ) method we have just used. We have used setPoint.X.ToString( ) to display the X value and setPoint.ToString( ) to display information about the object. All objects have a default .ToString() method included, even though we haven't written any code for it. At the moment, this code simply returns 'Object.Point', see figure 8.5.

Figure 8.5 The ToString( ) method

The ToString method is defined within the original C# Object class code and we have used that code. This is called 'inheritance' and we shall inherit our own code and data from our Point class in section 8.9.

8.5 Overriding

The ToString method doesn't provide much information. We will now write our own ToString method to provide more useful information about our class, overriding the default one.

Add the following code to the Point class (after '// end property Y'):

```
public override string ToString( )     // note the keyword 'override'
{
    return "My Point Object is at : " + _x + " " + _y;
}
```

Run the program. The message box now shows figure 8.6.

Figure 8.6 The overriden ToString( ) display

8.6 Adding Methods to a class

Apart from the ToString method, we haven't added any methods to our Point class yet. Let's now add a method called Move which moves the point a fixed distance one unit in both the X and Y directions.

We want the method to be accessible from everywhere, so it will be declared 'public'. Add the following code at the end of the Point class code, i.e. before '} // end class Point'.

```
public void Move( )  // move by one in both X and Y directions
{
   _x++;
   _y++;
} // end move
```

Add the following code to the button click code to move our setPoint (initially at 987,654). The code is:

```
setPoint.Move( );
MessageBox.Show(setPoint.ToString( ));
```

Run the code to see that setPoint is moved by one in the X and Y direction as shown in figure 8.7.

```
       " Y value = " +     y.ToString( ));
Point setPoint = new Point(987,654);
MessageBox.Show("X value = " + setPoint.X
       " Y value = " +    setPoint.Y.ToStrir

MessageBox.Show(setPoint.ToString());
setPoint.Move();
MessageBox.Show(setPoint.ToString());
```

My Point Object is at : 988 655

OK

Figure 8.7 Result of the Move method.

We can of course have private methods which would be accessible only from within our Point class. For instance if we wanted to, we could check if x and y were the same, or if one was zero, change its value.

8.7 Method overloading

As we did with the ToString method, we can also define methods with the same name but different parameters so that the method does similar (but different!) actions. This time we are declaring a second version of our own method and it's called method overloading. This is slightly different from overriding the ToString method, which replaced the method that was inherited from the original object code. It is similar to what we did with our constructors.

We shall now define a second Move method which accepts a distance to move passed to it as X and Y values.

Add the following code to the Point class

```
public void Move(int Xdistance, int Ydistance)
    {
        _x = _x + Xdistance;
        _y = _y + Ydistance;
    }
```

And add the following to the button click code:

```
setPoint.Move(-3,345);
MessageBox.Show(setPoint.ToString( ));
```

Run it to observe that the point does move, see figure 8.8.

Figure 8.8 Second Move method

Notice how the intelliSense editor knows about both of the Move methods as you type, see figure 8.9.

`firstPoint.Move(`

| ▲2 of 2▼ void Point.Move (**int X**, int Y) |

Figure 8.9 Intellisense method display

We will add some more methods later when we have extended our Point class to a circle.

8.8 Static classes

You may have noticed that we don't have to instantiate some objects with the 'new' keyword; we can just use them. For example the Math or MessageBox classes don't have to be instantiated. They are considered to be commonly used objects and so they don't have to be instantiated before use, have been declared with the keyword 'static',

A static class is useful for methods, like the Math class, that just perform an operation or read parameters and do not use get or set.

We could do same for our Point class, but it doesn't make sense as we want to create different points. However it might be useful if we wanted a 'Distance to origin' calculation available to all our objects.

We will create a new static class called Calculate to do this.

Add a new class to the project called Calculate. Within the class add a method called DistanceToOrigin. This will be our static class; note how this is declared in the code below. It will accept an X and Y position and return a double.

The complete object code is:

```
class Calculate
{
    public static double DistanceToOrigin(int x, int y)
    {
        return Math.Sqrt(x * x + y * y);
    }
}
```

Now add the following code for the button click to display the distance of our point from the origin:

```
MessageBox.Show ("Distance to Origin = "+
        Calculate.DistanceToOrigin(setPoint.X, setPoint.Y).ToString( ));
```

Note we do not have to instantiate Calculate or DistanceToOrigin. The result is shown in figure 8.10.

```
 Point setPoint = new Point(987,654);
MessageBox.Show("X value = " + setPoint.X.T
    " Y value = " +    setPoint.Y.ToString(

MessageBox.Show(setPoint.ToString());
setPoint.Move();
MessageBox.Show(setPoint.ToString());
setPoint.Move(-3, 345);
MessageBox.Show(setPoint.ToString());

MessageBox.Show("Distance to Origin = " +
    Calculate.DistanceToOrigin(setPoint.X, setPoint.Y).ToString());
```

Distance to Origin = 1403.64703540456

OK

Figure 8.10 Static class

8.9 Inheritance

Inheritance is a key concept in OOP. It allows you to create a new class that extends the behaviour of an existing class. We shall take our tried and tested Point code and create a new Circle class. A circle can be defined with three parameters: the X and Y point of the centre and a radius. Instead of creating a completely new Circle class which might introduce errors and take time to debug, we can use the Point class we have defined and extend it to create our Circle class. In other words the Circle object we create *inherits* the Point class's data and behaviours (and hopefully bug-free code).

To inherit from a class, the new class is defined followed by a colon and the class name to inherit from.

You've already seen this. If you look at the definition of Form1 in your C# code, you'll see a line of code similar to:

    public class Form1 : Form

The Form1 : Form part indicates that your Form1 inherits from the class Form.

Exercise: A circle class

Let's add a new class called Circle. Select Project > Add class. Name it Circle.
To define a class Circle which will inherit all the Point class information, we type:

    class Circle : Point
    {
    }

Change the code that has been written for you from class Circle to class Circle : Point, as above.

We can now instantiate a Circle object on the button click. To the button click code, add:

    Circle smallcircle = new Circle( );

The code will run and create a circle (actually a Point – a circle with no radius).

What we really want is to be able to define a Radius property for our circle and add methods such as Area or Circumference. Let's add constructor code, get and set Radius property code and an Area method code. Add these to your code as follows:

```
class Circle : Point
{
    // declare an internal, private radius variable
    private double _radius;

    public Circle( ) // implict constructor call comes here
    {
    }

    public Circle(int xValue, int yValue, double radiusValue)
    {
        // Circle constructor code _x and _y obtained from Point class
        _x = xValue;
        _y = yValue;
        // _x and _y must now be declared protected in Point class
        _radius = radiusValue;
    }

// property Radius
    public double Radius
    {
      get
      {
        return _radius;
      }
      set
      {
        if (value >= 0)    _radius = value;     // check for positive radius
      }
    }

// method Area
    public double Area()
    {
        return Math.PI * _radius * _radius;
    }

// override default ToString method
    public override string ToString( )
```

```
        {
            return "Circle at x,"+_x+" y,"+_y+" radius,"+_radius;
        }
    }
```

We have now added a Radius property for the circle. However, for the Circle class to be able to access the Point variables _x and _y, their declaration has to be changed to **protected** in the Point class code. You may have noticed the error messages when you typed the code. 'Protected' is halfway between public and private declaration and allows access from with the class it is declared, but also any class derived from it.

Therefore, change the point class _x and _y declaration to protected, as follows:

```
    // Point coordinates
    protected int _x, _y;
```

We can now instantiate a default circle with no X, Y or Radius properties defined, or instantiate a circle with X, Y and Radius values. We can alter the X, Y and Radius properties and calculate the circle's radius. Try the following code for the button click

```
Circle smallCircle = new Circle( );          // default circle
Circle largeCircle = new Circle(12, 34, 56);  // set x,y and radius
smallCircle.X = 98;                           // set smallCircle X
smallCircle.Y = 87;                           // set smallCircle Y
smallCircle.Radius = 11;                       // set smallCircle Radius
MessageBox.Show(smallCircle.ToString( ));     // and display
MessageBox.Show(largeCircle.ToString( ));
MessageBox.Show(smallCircle.Area( ).ToString( ));
```

Notice also that your circle object has access to the Point class Move method. You can move your circle around the same way you can move your points.

8.10 Overriding methods

We have seen how we can override the ToString method. If we want to allow any of the class methods we have defined to be overridden, their declaration must be changed to **virtual**. For instance, the Area method we defined could be overridden by passing an extra parameter to calculate the volume of a cylinder.

8.11 Self Assessment Exercises

1. Watch the supporting videos pointed to at Elektor's web site.

2. Create a class for a Square with properties Height and Width and a method Area(). Write the code to get and set the Height and Width and calculate the Area. Provide some checks, so that negative values can't be used.

3. Create objects of your Square class (create squares) and change the square's properties in the code. Call the Area method and display it.

4. Overwrite the default .ToString() method to provide more useful information on your object.

5. Create a new class called 'Box' which inherits from Square and has an extra property 'Depth' and a new method called 'Volume' which overrides the Area method.

6. Create an object called Vehicle. It could have properties such as Bus, Car, Train, etc. Each could have a make, number of wheels and passengers etc. You could declare a public variable called 'PetrolPrice' and a static method PricePerKm.

7. Can you think how this might be overloaded to produce a Transport object with say a method PassengerPricePerKm?

8. Look at the other methods that are inherited from the Class code (Equals, GetHashCode, GetType) and find out what they mean.

9. Create a new class 'Cylinder' which inherits from the Circle and has an extra property 'Height' and method 'Volume'. Override the Area method to create a Volume method.

10. If you want to find out more about OOP, look up the terms: base class and derived class and polymorphism.

8.12 Summary

This chapter has covered writing classes and creating objects from a class. We defined a class called Point and created objects of this class using the 'new' keyword. The class has properties and methods which are parts of the object. The class properties are altered by the get and set methods and accessed from the main code using the dot notation. We have seen how an object is instantiated using a default constructor and we have created our own constructor that initializes the object's properties. The default ToString method has be overridden by our own method. We created an overloaded version of the method and have seen how the methods run.

Static classes, which don't have to be instantiated, have been covered. These are useful for methods which just access values or perform calculations.

Finally, Circle objects were created from a Circle class which inherited from the Point class. To do this we had to declare protected variables and virtual methods.

Chapter 9 - File handling and menu dialogs

9.1 Introduction

After the fairly intensive chapter on Object Oriented Programming let's return to more practical work.

Sooner or later you will want to save or read information on disk. Disk files are used for a wide variety of reasons; to hold temporary or permanent data, set-up or user information etc. Data logging applications can easily collect large amounts of data which may be saved on disk before analysed or transmitted elsewhere. Sometimes it is easier to save data on a disk than to deal with databases. In this chapter we will look at file types and the C# controls to handle them. We will look at databases later.

9.2 File Types - Text (ASCII) or Binary

Files are either text files (ASCII or similar) or non-text (binary) files.

9.2.1 Text Files

Text files simply contain ASCII (or UTF-8) characters, i.e. those that can be typed from the keyboard. These are often strings terminated with Carriage Return (CR, 0x0D or '\r') and Line Feed characters (LF, 0x0A or '\n'). Basic text editors create this sort of file. Most applications can handle text files and it is a good way of transferring data between applications. These files are normally handled in a line-by-line or sequential manner.

9.2.2 Binary Files - Typed and Untyped files

Binary files contain all values (i.e. printable and non-printable characters) and can't be displayed directly on the screen. Binary files are either *typed* or *untyped*. *Typed* files have a known format using data types, e.g. the structure seen in section 5.3. *Untyped* files have no rigid structure and record sizes can vary. Application (.EXE) program files and bitmap graphic files (.BMP) are good examples of these. In this case the application dealing with the file knows about the file structure and how to deal with it.

9.3 File Dialog Boxes and MenuStrip control

We shall start by looking at the C# File handling controls and Menus which make it easy to open and save files.

The .NET framework provides File and Directory classes which can be used to read and write files and these are covered later. Before that however, we shall look at the controls available to handle files.

Visual Studio environment provides dialogs to open, save and print files on the dialogs and printing toolbox. These are normally displayed using a menu system, and the MenuStrip control is used to create these. The relevant controls are shown in figure 9.1.

Figure 9.1 The MenuStrip and FileDialog controls

To open and save files, place the OpenFileDialog and SaveFileDialog controls on the form. They are non-visual controls (i.e. not part of the form), so will be placed at the bottom of the form's display area. You have used these whenever you have opened or saved files. They are displayed by executing code and we will create a menu which will do this.

9.3.1 The MenuStrip control - a simple RichTextBox editor

The MenuStrip control on the 'Menus and Toolbars' toolbox group is used to create the typical 'File, Edit, View .. Help' menu that many Windows programs have.

Let's study these with an exercise and create a simple text editor using the RichTextBox control. This application use a MenuStrip control to display a main menu like Word with File > Open and File > Save options, and use the familiar File handling dialogs.

- Start a new Windows Application and give it a suitable name (e.g. TextEditor).

- Add the OpenFileDialog and SaveFileDialog controls to the form (they will be placed in the status area)
- Place a MenuStrip control on the form. This invites you to type a heading, or you can add further MenuItems, a ComboBox or a TextBox, see figure 9.2.

Figure 9.2 Menu Designer

We want to have a File heading here, so just type 'File' and press return. You can now enter the items for this drop down menu. Type 'Open' and 'Save'. If you hold the mouse over the menu item you will see a down arrow which as before, allows you to add further menu items, combo boxes, and text items or a separator.

- Add a separator and a File > Exit option. If you want to you can add a File > New option. If you make a mistake clicking away from the menu will tidy things up for you.

Let's add an Help > About menu. Add a further menu item to the right of the File menu and call it '&Help'. You will notice that the ampersand causes the 'H' in Help to be underlined and can be used as a short-cut item when your program runs.

Add an '&About' item under the Help menu.

- Finally add a Rich Text box from the Common Controls toolbox group. This is where the file that is opened will be displayed. A Rich Text box provides more functionality than a text box including edit methods such as Find, Cut, Copy and Paste, and file handling methods LoadFile and SaveFile.

Your design should be similar to figure 9.3:

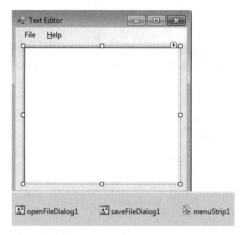

Figure 9.3 Text Editor User interface

Now we have to write the code for each of the menu items (File > Open) etc. Let's see how we can use the menu to open and save a file.

9.3.2 The OpenFileDialog

The OpenFile and SaveFile dialogs appear when an application such as Word opens or saves a file, so your user should be familiar with them, see figure 9.4. They are not permanently visible controls and appear when a 'ShowDialog' method is executed.

Figure 9.4 File Open Dialog

To add the File Open dialog, on the MenuStrip control click 'File' then double-click 'Open' to display the code for openToolStripMenuItem_Click.

The following code clears the richTextBox, sets up the openFileDialog properties and displays the open file dialog. Add this for the menuStrip 'File>Open' click code.

```
private void openToolStripMenuItem_Click(object sender, EventArgs e)
{
    // clear rich text box
    richTextBox1.Clear();

    // Set open file dialog initial directory and title
    openFileDialog1.InitialDirectory = @"C:\";
    openFileDialog1.Title = "Please select a file";

    // open the dialog and check for cancel
    if (openFileDialog1.ShowDialog( ) != DialogResult.Cancel)
    {
        // not cancelled - read file
        richTextBox1.LoadFile(openFileDialog1.FileName,
            RichTextBoxStreamType.PlainText);
    }
    else
    {
        MessageBox.Show("You pressed cancel");
    }
}
```

This code sets the initial directory of the open file dialog to C: and gives a title prompt. The @ symbol is used to treat the string literally (it means you don't have to put double backslash). The dialog is displayed when the openFileDialog.ShowDialog( ) method is executed. If the operation isn't cancelled, the file is read using the RichTextBox 'LoadFile' method.

We have set up some of the open file dialog properties such as InitialDirectory in the code, but of course we could set the properties at design time. You might like to take this opportunity to look at the OpenFileDialog properties and methods.

As the user will browse to select a file, it is unlikely there will be any errors. We could put this code into a try and catch construct to check for errors however. But see also section 9.3.5.

9.3.3 The SaveFileDialog

To save the file we will use the SaveFileDialog and the rich text box method 'SaveFile'. You might want your code to check if the file already exists and check for overwriting the file. These are properties of the SaveFileDialog control which can be selected, and so we don't have to write code for them. Add the following for the File Save click:

```
private void saveToolStripMenuItem_Click(object sender, EventArgs e)
{
    if (saveFileDialog1.ShowDialog() != DialogResult.Cancel)
    {
        // not cancelled - write file
        richTextBox1.SaveFile(saveFileDialog1.FileName,
            RichTextBoxStreamType.PlainText);
    }
    else
    {
        MessageBox.Show("You pressed cancel");
    }
}
```

Finally, for the File > Exit commands add the following code:

```
private void exitToolStripMenuItem_Click(object sender, EventArgs e)
{
    Application.Exit( );          // but you might like to give a warning
}
```

Save the project and run the program. Select a text (.TXT) file to see it displayed in the list box. You can save the file under another name, or change the text in the memo box and save it. You have created a simple editor.

If you want to see how a binary file is displayed, try selecting an Application (.EXE) file.

9.3.4 Open and Save Dialog Box properties

At this stage, the dialog boxes display all the file types. You might want to limit the file types that the user can see. It's not really necessary for our editor program to display anything other than text files and possibly 'All files'. To select specific files such as *.TXT, the filter property is used. The filter can be set in the properties or by code. To select files in code, try the following code:

```
openFileDialog1.Filter = "All files (*.*)|*.*|Text files(*.TXT)|*.txt";
```

The same string is entered into the Filter property if you want to set it at design time.

You can try adding word documents (add Word docs|*.DOC) and open one to see how it is displayed.

Repeat for the Save Dialog component and save the project. You can now run the program. Selecting File > Open will display the Open Dialog box, only text (.TXT) files only are shown and can be selected.

Save the file with a different name and directory. Close the application using File > Exit and using your favourite editor, prove to yourself that the file has indeed been copied to a different directory.

9.3.5 File error handling

Currently, if the user types in an invalid filename rather than selecting one from the folder, an error message is shown. Setting the CheckFileExists property of the OpenFileDialog control to 'true' will prevent this. There are many other properties which you might find useful to try out, including 'CheckPathExists', 'DefaultExt' and 'AddExtension' (you might like to add the extension TXT and see what happens).

Remember you can put your file handling code in a try-catch block (see chapter 6) which can deal with errors that may occur.

9.4 Adding Menu items - About box

The Help > About menu item hasn't been added. Let's do that. An About form is one of the forms available from the C# menus.

Select Project> Add Windows Form, choose Windows Forms from the templates and select About Box from the offerings.
An About Box is displayed, which you can modify to suit, see figure 9.5.

Figure 9.5 The About Box

If you try changing the AboutBox labels you will find that when the program runs they aren't displayed. This is because the AboutBox information is extracted from the program's assembly information, found in the Solution Explorer, see figure 9.6. The picture however can be changed the same way the picture box icon was selected.

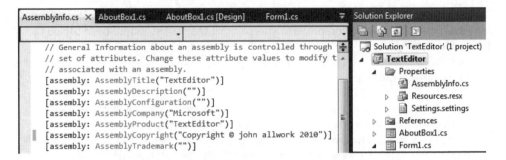

Figure 9.6. The About box information

You should not change the Assembly.cs code, you should change the project assembly information using Project > *name* > Application > Assembly Information, see figure 9.7.

Figure 9.7 Assembly Information

The About box is displayed the same way we displayed a second form in chapter 3. Add the following code for the Help > About menu item

```
private void aboutToolStripMenuItem_Click(object sender, EventArgs e)
{
    AboutBox1 frmAbout = new AboutBox1( );
    frmAbout.Show( );
}
```

The OK button doesn't close the About box. Double-click the OK button and change the code to the following:

```
private void okButton_Click(object sender, EventArgs e)
{
    this.Close();
}
```

9.5 PrintDialog boxes

A file can be printed using the PrintDialog and PrintDocument controls found on the Printing toolbox controls. The PrintDialog requests the printer you want to use, the page range, number of copies, etc and is displayed with the ShowDialog() method. The PrintDocument contains the event that prints the document.

If you want further information on this, search Help for the PrintDocument Class.

9.6 RichTextBox editor: cut, paste copy and find

The rich text box also has methods for cut, copy and paste. All you have to do is add menu items for these, e.g. Edit> Cut and Edit >Paste, and add the following code:

```
private void cutToolStripMenuItem_Click(object sender, EventArgs e)
{
    richTextBox1.Cut();
}

private void pasteToolStripMenuItem_Click(object sender, EventArgs e)
{
    richTextBox1.Paste();
}
```

Run your program, type some text into the rich text box and select some of it. Edit > Cut will remove the selection and Edit > Paste will replace it. Edit > Copy works in a similar way.

For the Find, you have to choose the text to find. Add an Edit > Find menu item and the following code for the click event. The code finds the text 'Text', matching its case and changes the selection to Verdana, 12, italic, blue.

```
private void findToolStripMenuItem_Click(object sender, EventArgs e)
{
    richTextBox1.Find("Text",RichTextBoxFinds.MatchCase);
    richTextBox1.SelectionFont = new Font ("Verdana", 12, FontStyle.Italic);
    richTextBox1.SelectionColor = Color.Blue;
}
```

9.7 File and Directory classes

Your program might not need to request file details from the user and you can use the File and Directory classes directly. These provide methods for the creation, copying, deletion, moving and opening of files. They are static methods and don't have to be instantiated.

Many of the File methods return another I/O type (e.g. StreamReader) when the file is created or opened. This is then used to access the file.

The main File methods are:

AppendText	Creates a StreamWriter that appends text to an existing file.
Copy	Copies an existing file to a new file.
Create	Creates a file in the specified path.
Delete	Deletes the specified file.
Exists	Determines whether the specified file exists.
Move	Moves a file to a new folder.
Open	Opens a FileStream on the specified path.
OpenRead	Opens an existing file for reading.
OpenText	Opens an existing text file for reading.
OpenWrite	Opens an existing file for writing.
ReadAllBytes	Opens a binary file, reads the file into a byte array and closes the file.
ReadAllLines	Opens a text file, reads all its lines into a string array and closes the file.
ReadAllText	Opens a text file, reads all lines of the file into a string and closes the file.
Replace	Replaces the contents of the file with the contents of another file, deleting the original file and creating a backup.
WriteAllBytes	Creates a new file, writes the specified byte array to the file and then closes the file. If the target file exists, it is overwritten.
WriteAllLines	Creates a new file, writes the specified string to the file and then closes the file. If the target file exists, it is overwritten.
WriteAllText	Creates a new file, write the contents to the file and closes the file. If the target file exists, it is overwritten.

The main Directory methods are:

CreateDirectory	Creates all the directories in a specified path.
Delete	Deletes a specified directory.
Exists	Determines whether the directory exists.
Move	Moves a file or a directory and its contents to a new location.

The FileStream class is used to read from, write to, open and close files on a file system. It provides access to a Stream, a class that provides byte read and write to a file, but could also be an I/O device, or as well shall see an internet socket.

StreamReader and StreamWriter classes are used to read and write text files (utf-8), and BinaryReader and BinaryWriter classes in the case of binary data.

Remember to add 'using System.IO' if you want to use these classes.

9.8 File handling example

Here are two examples of writing and reading to files using the File and Directory classes. The first uses StreamWriter and StreamReader classes to create a text file and read it back, and the second uses File and Directory classes to check if they exist and then FileStream, BinaryWriter and BinaryReader to write binary data to a file, then read it back:

9.8.1 Using StreamWriter and StreamReader objects

The following example creates a StreamWriter object to write text to a file and then creates a StreamReader object to read it.

```
StreamWriter sw = new StreamWriter("Test.txt");
// Add some text to the file.
sw.Write("Hello ");          // no CRLF
sw.WriteLine("World!");      // add CRLF
sw.WriteLine("------------------");
sw.Close();

// The using statement also closes the StreamReader.
using (StreamReader sr = new StreamReader("Test.txt"))
{
    MessageBox.Show(sr.ReadLine());  // Displays 'Hello world!'
    MessageBox.Show(sr.ReadLine());  // Displays '-----------'
}
```

The file can be checked by reading it in Notepad.

9.8.2 Using BinaryReader and BinaryWriter objects.

The following example creates a BinaryWriter object to write binary values text to a file and then creates a BinaryReader object to read the data.

```
string dirPath = @"c:/Temp";

// Create the folder c:\temp if it doesn't exist
if (!Directory.Exists(dirPath))
{
    Directory.CreateDirectory(dirPath);
```

```
    }

    string fileName = @dirPath + "/TestFile.bin";
    // create and binary file if it doesn't exist
    if (!File.Exists(fileName))
    {
        // file doesn't exist - create file

        FileStream fs = new FileStream(fileName, FileMode.CreateNew);
        BinaryWriter bw = new BinaryWriter(fs);
        byte[] byteArray = { 0x48, 0x45, 0x4C, 0x4C, 0x4F }; // hello!

        for (int i = 0; i < byteArray.Length; i++)
        {
            bw.Write(byteArray[i]);
        }

        bw.Close();
        fs.Close();
    }

    // and read it back

    FileStream fsRead = new FileStream(fileName, FileMode.Open);
    BinaryReader br = new BinaryReader(fsRead);

    for (int i = 0; i < fsRead.Length; i++)
    {
        MessageBox.Show(br.ReadByte().ToString());
    }

    br.Close();
    fsRead.Close();
```

Note that as this file contains ASCII characters ('hello'), it can also be read by notepad.

9.9 Self Assessment Exercises

1. Add Print commands to the menu strip and your editor. If you need more information try searching in Help.

2, Add the cut, copy, paste commands to your editor.

3. Add Find and Replace commands to your editor.

4. Write a program to open a text file and save the individual high and low 4 bit nibbles of each byte and in a binary file. Write a program to do the reverse, i.e. reads two bytes from a binary file, combines them and writes them as a text file.

9.10 Summary

In this chapter we have looked at text and binary file types. We have seen the MenuStrip component and looked at the openFileDialog and saveFileDialogs. A simple editor was created using the versatile rich text box to load and save files. The editor was extended to provide print, cut, paste and find commands. Finally we looked at File and Directory classes and saw how to read and write both text and binary files using StreamWriter and StreamReader classes and FileStream, BinaryWriter and BinaryReader classes.

Chapter 10 - Graphics and Multimedia

10.1 Introduction

Your user interface can be made more impressive if it uses images and graphics. We have seen the picture box control which can display images. There are no graphics controls such as rectangle or ellipse that can be placed directly on the form; they have to be drawn by your code. In this chapter we will see how to draw graphics objects. We shall also look at the Media Player control.

10.2 Drawing Graphics

The basic procedure for drawing text or graphics is as follows: A Graphics object is created on a form or container such as a panel where the graphics is to be drawn. A pen or brush object is defined, and then Graphics methods are called to draw or paint lines and shapes. The pen is used to draw lines and the brush to fill areas. The Graphics object is in the System.Drawing namespace.

Exercise: Line Drawing.

Let's see how we draw lines with an example that draws a line on a panel on a form.

Start a new application and place a panel on the form. So you can see the panel, change its BorderStyle property to FixedSingle. Find the panel's MouseDown event and change it to the following code:

```
private void panel1_MouseDown(object sender, MouseEventArgs e)
{
    System.Drawing.Graphics grpObject;
    grpObject = this.panel1.CreateGraphics( );
    Pen objmyPen = new Pen(System.Drawing.Color.Blue);
    grpObject.DrawLine(objmyPen, 0, 0, 100, 100);
}
```

In this code the graphics object (grpObject) is created on panel1. A Pen object is created (objmyPen) in Blue. Note the American spelling for colour. The DrawLine method uses the Pen object to draw between two x and y points: in this case from 0, 0 to 100, 100. Remember, you should add 'using System.Drawing' at the top of your code.

Run the program and click on the panel. A blue line should be drawn from top left to bottom right of the panel as shown in figure 10.1. Note that point (0,0) is the top left, with increasing X values moving right and increasing Y values moving down the screen.

Figure 10.1 Drawing on a panel

10.3 The Paint event.

Unfortunately the line doesn't stay drawn if the form is minimized and then redisplayed. In this example the line is only drawn when the panel is clicked and not when the panel is redisplayed. We may need to draw the line when our form is redrawn. The panel and the form controls have a paint event which occurs when the control is redrawn. We will now use this event to draw a line.

Find the paint event for the panel in the properties window and change it to the following code:

```
private void panel1_Paint(object sender, PaintEventArgs e)
{
    // draw red line
  System.Drawing.Graphics grpObject = e.Graphics;
    Pen objmyPen = new Pen(System.Drawing.Color.Red);
    grpObject.DrawLine(objmyPen, 0, 100, 100, 0);
}
```

Run the code. When the panel is drawn, its Paint event occurs and a red line is drawn on the panel from bottom left to top right. Click the panel to draw the blue line. Now minimize and redisplay the form; the original blue line disappears, but the red line is still drawn by the paint event.

Note in this case how the graphics object (e.Graphics) was obtained from the PaintEventArgs parameter passed to the panel's paint event.

You should dispose of your objects when you have finished with them. To do so use the code:

```
objmyPen.Dispose( );
```

If you need to redraw your graphics from your code you should not call the Paint event, but instead call the Invalidate method. This invalidates the object which will then be redrawn by Windows:

```
panel1.Invalidate( );
```

10.4 Drawing on the form

When the form is opened or revealed, the objects on it are drawn by the paint event. You can prove this by displaying a message with MessageBox.Show in the Form_Paint event:

```
private void Form1_Paint(object sender, PaintEventArgs e)
{
    MessageBox.Show("In Form1_Paint");
}
```

If you wish to draw on your form you can either add code to this event or you can write your own OnPaint event, overriding the original.

For example, add the following OnPaint method

```
protected override void OnPaint(PaintEventArgs e)
{
    Graphics grpObject = e.Graphics;
    Pen objmyPen = new Pen(System.Drawing.Color.Blue);
    grpObject.DrawLine(objmyPen, 0, 0, 100, 100);
}
```

The Paint event (now your OnPaint code) is triggered when the form is opened or displayed and hence the graphics is drawn every time; it doesn't disappear. Note however, that resizing the form doesn't trigger the form's Paint event.

You can still call the original Form's Paint code from your OnPaint method if you add the following code:

```
base.OnPaint(e);
```

In this code the term 'base' refers to the base class, in this case the Form. This code calls the form's original Paint code, which we had previously overridden.

If you want to prove it, add the code base.OnPaint(e); to the protected OnPaint event and see what happens. The message only appears if the base.OnPaint(e); code is present and appears when the form is resized or redisplayed.

Try using OnPaint(e); instead of base.OnPaint(e); and see what happens. (You will get a stack overflow error – why?). Can you also use Form1_Paint(null, e); instead of base.OnPaint(e); ?

If you need your graphics to stay on the form then you can do it in one of two ways:

- Place all the code in the form's Paint event. This is best if you are drawing only a few items.
- Draw to a memory bitmap and copy the bitmap to the form in the form's Paint event. This is more complicated and better if you are doing a lot of drawing, but beyond the scope of this book.

10.5 The Pen

As we have seen, the Pen is used to draw lines and we shall use it to draw shapes such as rectangles, circles, ellipses and polygons later. A Pen object is created and it controls the appearance of the lines drawn. The main Pen properties are:

- Color - This is specified by setting the individual values for Alpha, Red, Green and Blue (ARGB). Alpha defines the transparency of the colour and is optional. Each ARGB value can be from $0 – 255$. For the RGB values 0, 0, 0 (0x0) is black and 255, 255, 255 (0xFFF) is white.
- Width - The width in pixels of the line drawn.
- DashStyle - Specifies the pattern of the line (Solid, Dash, Dot, DashDot, Custom, etc.)

Once a pen object has been created its colour, width, style etc can be changed as shown in the following example code fragment:

```
System.Drawing.Graphics grpObject;
grpObject = this.panel1.CreateGraphics();
  // create blue pen 5 pixels wide
Pen objmyPen = new Pen(System.Drawing.Color.Blue, 5);
grpObject.DrawLine(objmyPen, 0, 0, 100, 100);

// chage Width
objmyPen.Width = 3;

// chage style to dashed
objmyPen.DashStyle =
        System.Drawing.Drawing2D.DashStyle.DashDotDot;

// change to semi-transparent red
objmyPen.Color = System.Drawing.Color.FromArgb(128, 255, 0, 0);
grpObject.DrawLine(objmyPen, 0, 100, 100, 0);
```

Note that the FromARGB( ) method has been used to set the alpha and RGB values. The program output is shown in figure 10.2.

Figure 10.2 Pen drawing program output

10.6 The Brush

The brush object defines how areas are filled. Like the Pen, the brush object has to be created and its main properties are its colour and style.

- The Color determines the colour of the filled shapes, including foreground and background colours.
- The Style determines if the area is filled with a solid colour or a line style. Some styles are:
  HatchBrush (uses a foreground and background colour),
  LinearGradientBrush (blends one colour into another),
  SolidBrush (fills with one colour),
  TextureBrush (uses an Image).

10.7 Drawing Text

Text is drawn with DrawString( ) method. You state the text string, the font and brush style together with the X and Y position of the text, for example:

```
private void panel1_Paint(object sender, PaintEventArgs e)
{
  Graphics grpObject = e.Graphics;
  Font myFont = new Font("Arial", 16);
  SolidBrush myBrush = new SolidBrush(Color.Green);
  grpObject.DrawString("Mystring", myFont, myBrush, 20, 30);
}
```

10.8 Basic Shapes

Methods are provided for graphics objects to draw ellipses and rectangles (and hence circles and squares). Having created a graphics object as we did above, the methods can be used. We have seen the DrawString( ) method. You can let the Intellisense prompt display them, see figure 10.3.

Figure 10.3 Graphics object drawing methods

Other basic graphic methods are:

DrawRectangle (Pen p, int X, int Y, int width, int height);

This draws a rectangle with pen p, at X, Y, with width and height.

DrawEllipse (Pen p, int X, int Y, int width, int height);

This draws an ellipse with Pen p, bounded by the rectangle defined by top left hand point X, Y with width and height.

FillRectangle (Brush b, int X, int Y, int width, int height);

This draws a filled rectangle with brush b, bounded by the rectangle defined by top left hand point X, Y with width and height.

FillEllipse(Brush b, int X, int Y, int width, int height);

This draws a filled ellipse with brush b, bounded by the rectangle defined by top left hand point X, Y with width and height.

For more detail on drawing shapes, refer to the self assessment exercises. This has an example which draws a different shape and colour each time the form is painted as shown in figure 10.4.

Figure 10.4 Shape program output

10.9 Other shapes - arcs, pies, polylines and polygons.

Other shapes such as arcs, pie, filled pie, polylines, polygons and filled polygons can also be drawn. The basic graphic methods for these are defined as follows.

DrawArc(Pen p, int X, int Y, int width, int height, int startAngle, int sweepAngle);

This uses the Pen and draws an arc of an ellipse from startAngle in degrees, sweeping by sweepAngle, bounded by the rectangle defined by top left hand point X, Y with width and height.

There are many variations of all of these methods. The Rectangle object can also be used as the bounding area. This replaces the 'x, y, width, height' code, for instance:

Rectangle myRect = new Rectangle(0,0,200,100);

This defines a rectangle with at 0,0 and a width of 200 and height of 100. The DrawArc code is:

grpObject.DrawArc(objmyPen, myRect, 0, 45);

The DrawPie draws a pie section with the same parameters as the DrawArc.

DrawPie (Pen p, int X, int Y, int width, int height, int startAngle, int sweepAngle);

Arcs and Pies are drawn in a clockwise manner, with 0^0 being along the +X-axis. The following code draws the pie section shown in figure 10.5, bound by a box at x=0, y=0, width = 100, height=100, start angle = 0 and sweep angle =45°.

DrawPie(objmyPen, 0, 0, 100, 100, 0, 45);

Figure 10.5 A Pie section

FillPie (Brush b, int X, int Y, int width, int height, int startAngle, int sweepAngle);

Similar to DrawPie, except a filled Pie is drawn using the brush.

Polylines and Polygons (a closed series of Polylines) are best drawn using the Polyline and Polygon methods. These methods draw a series of lines connecting points which are passed to the method in an ArrayList. A filled polygon can also be drawn using the FillPolygon method.

The self assessment exercises have an example on drawing Polygons. In the exercise the user clicks the mouse to define the X and Y positions for the polygon's points, and produces a display similar to figure 10.6.

Figure 10.5 Polygon program output

10.10 Reading and writing a single pixel

There is no graphics command to read or write a single pixel. You could draw a line from (x, y) to (x, y+1), but that draws two pixels.

To read or write to a pixel on the screen you have to import some DLL methods from gdi32 (see chapter 18.6). The calls are CreateDC, DeleteDC, SetPixel and GetPixel.

To draw on the screen you have to 'borrow' it from Windows. To do this you have to create a device context (using CreateDC) and return it when finished (using DeleteDC). CreateDC returns a pointer to the drawing object, which is used by SetPixel and GetPixel.

The following code displays the colour value of a panel when it is clicked and then generates a new random background colour for it.

At the top of your code, add the declaration 'using System.Runtime.InteropServices;'

Add the following DLLImport code before 'public Form1':

```
// DLL to create a device context for a resource.
[DllImport("gdi32.dll")]
public static extern IntPtr CreateDC(string strDriver, string strDevice,
string strOutput, IntPtr pData);

// DLL to release the resource
[DllImport("gdi32.dll")]
public static extern bool DeleteDC(IntPtr hdc);

// DLL to set a pixel - pass DC pointer, x, y and colour
[DllImport("gdi32.dll")]
static extern uint SetPixel(IntPtr hdc, int X, int Y, uint crColor);

// DLL to get pixel value - pass DC pointer, x and y, colour value is
returned
[DllImport("gdi32.dll")]
public static extern uint GetPixel(IntPtr hdc, int nXPos, int nYPos);
```

Place a panel on a form and enter the following code for its mouse down event:

```
private void panel1_MouseDown(object sender, MouseEventArgs e)
{

// Obtain a Device Context for the panel.
IntPtr ptrScreen = CreateDC("Display", null, null, IntPtr.Zero);

// and use it to obtain the pixel value of the mouse position
// GetPixel
int pixelValue = (int)GetPixel(ptrScreen, e.X, e.Y);

// and release it
DeleteDC(ptrScreen);

// Convert the pixel value colour to a .NET Color object
```

```
Color clr = Color.FromArgb((pixelValue & 0x000000FF),
  (pixelValue & 0x0000FF00) >> 8,
  (pixelValue & 0x00FF0000) >> 16);

string str = "red: " + clr.R +" green: " + clr.G + "blue: " + clr.B;
MessageBox.Show(str);

// generate new panel background colour
Random rndObj = new Random();
int red = rndObj.Next(255);
int green = rndObj.Next(255);
int blue = rndObj.Next(255);
panel1.BackColor = Color.FromArgb(red, green, blue);
}
```

Note the use of e.X and e.Y from MouseEventArgs to obtain the X and Y position of the mouse.

Color.FromArgb creates a Color structure, clr, from the 8-bit alpha, red, green, and blue pixel values. Here we only use RGB. Note that having got a Color value, you can extract the individual ARGB values; see the use of clr.R. The program creates the new background colour using Color.FromArgb from three random

You can also set a pixel in the same way. The following code snippet writes to the screen on the panel's mouse move event. Note that the X and Y positions are obtained from the panel, and they are used as X and Y positions to write to the screen (not the panel).

```
private void panel1_MouseMove(object sender, MouseEventArgs e)
{
  Random rndObj = new Random();
  int red = rndObj.Next(255);
  int green = rndObj.Next(255);
  int blue = rndObj.Next(255);
  // Obtain a Device Context for the Display.
  IntPtr ptrScreen = CreateDC("Display", null, null, IntPtr.Zero);
  // and use it to obtain the pixel value of the mouse position

  // SetPixel
  SetPixel(ptrScreen, e.X, e.Y, (uint)((red << 16) | (green << 8) | (blue)));
  // and release resource
  DeleteDC(ptrScreen);
}
```

10.11 Drawing Graphs and Charts

If you want to draw a graph or chart, you can either draw your own or obtain some third party software. We will study drawing graphs using a third party package called NPlot in chapter 17.

If you want a simple 2D chart, there is an example at the Coding4Fun site at:
http://msdn.microsoft.com/coding4fun/someassemblyrequired/hotinhere/default.aspx

Some free chart controls are also available. If you need these, you can try:
http://www.carlosag.net/Tools/WebChart/Default.aspx

10.12 Multimedia applications

The MediaPlayer control is used to control playing or recording devices such as audio or video CD-ROM/DVD player.

The MediaPlayer control, see figure 10.7, provides a screen and controls to manage the media (play, pause, stop, etc.)

Figure 10.7 MediaPlayer control

The mediaPlayer control needs to be added to the toolbox before it can be used.
To do this, right-click the Toolbox menu and select 'Choose Items', see figure 10.8.

Figure 10.8 Choose Toolbox items

This displays 'Choose toolbox items'. Select the COM (component object model) controls tab and scroll to Windows Media Player, see figure 10.9.

Figure 10.9 COM Component Toolbox items

Tick the box and add the component. It should appear in the toolbox, figure 10.10.

Figure 10.10 Adding Media Player

Add the Player to the form and resize it to show the controls and the screen. Its default name is 'axWindowsMediaPlayer1'.

Add a button and change its Text to 'Load Video'. Add the following code for the click event:

```
axWindowsMediaPlayer1.URL = @"c:\windows\clock.avi";
```

The @ symbol instructs the compiler to ignore backslashes which would otherwise be interpreted as an escape sequence. Make sure the file exists. You could add a file dialog box to search for media files.

Your GUI should be similar to figure 10.11:

Figure 10.11 The MediaPlayer GUI

The media will start when you set the URL, but you can control the video from your application, for example you could have:

      axWindowsMediaPlayer1.Ctlcontrols.stop( );

or

      axWindowsMediaPlayer1.Ctlcontrols.play( );

If you don't want the player controls to be displayed, set the uiMode property to 'none'. You can also turn the screen off if by making it invisible. E.g:

      axWindowsMediaPlayer1.uiMode = "none";
      axWindowsMediaPlayer1.uiMode = "invisible;

You can also have a mini or custom controls display.

Note: if you copy the multimedia file to your program folder, you can move files between computers if you use relative addressing and change the filename's drive (C:) and path (..\Demos\etc.)

If you have problems installing the Media Player, or want to distribute your multimedia application, you need to add a couple of files to your application. See the following reference for more details:

      http://msdn.microsoft.com/en-us/library/dd564585(VS.85).aspx

10.12.1 MediaPlayer events

If you want to loop your sound or video, you have to detect the event which tells you the media has finished playing and restart your media. Find the PlayStateChanged event and add the following code to loop the media:

```
private void axWindowsMediaPlayer1_PlayStateChange
(object sender, AxWMPLib._WMPOCXEvents_PlayStateChangeEvent e)

    {
        axWindowsMediaPlayer1.Ctlcontrols.play();
    }
```

10.13 Self Assessment Exercises

Try the following exercises

1. The Paint method

Place a panel on the form. Add MessageBox.Show methods to the panel's paint event and the form's paint event and observe the paint's operation. Override the form's paint event with your own OnPaint method, which should also have a MessageBox.Show method. Notice that the original form's paint method no longer runs. Add a base.OnPaint(e); code and see that the form's paint method is now called.

2. Drawing shapes

As an exercise in drawing the different shapes, type in the following code for the form's OnPaint overridden event. It draws a different shape and colour each time the form is painted as shown in figure 10.5.

```
protected override void OnPaint(PaintEventArgs e)
{
    Graphics grpObject = e.Graphics;              // create Graphics object
    Pen objmyPen = new Pen(System.Drawing.Color.Blue);    // define Pen
    SolidBrush myBrush = new SolidBrush(Color.Red);        // and brush
    Font arial = new Font("Arial", 12);                    // and font

    Random RandomNumber =  new Random();   // define random number
    int rndNo = RandomNumber.Next(4);      // get random value 0 to 3

    switch (rndNo)                         // get random brush color
    {
        case 0: myBrush.Color = Color.Red; break;
        case 1: myBrush.Color = Color.Blue; break;
        case 2: myBrush.Color = Color.Orange; break;
        case 3: myBrush.Color = Color.Green; break;
    }

    rndNo = RandomNumber.Next(4);          // get random value 0 to 3
    switch (rndNo)                         // get random pen color
```

```
    {
        case 0: objmyPen.Color = Color.DarkOrchid; break;
        case 1: objmyPen.Color = Color.Tomato; break;
        case 2: objmyPen.Color = Color.Peru; break;
        case 3: objmyPen.Color = Color.AliceBlue; break;
    }

    rndNo = RandomNumber.Next(7);           // get random number 0-6
    int rndX = RandomNumber.Next(100);      // get random X and Y
    int rndY = RandomNumber.Next(100);      // values for end point
    string drawnstr=null;                   // string for DrawString

    switch (rndNo)                          // draw random shape at 0,0
    {
        case 0:                             // draw line
            grpObject.DrawLine(objmyPen, 0, 0, (float)rndX,(float)rndY);
            drawnstr = "Line to ";
            break;
        case 1:                             // draw rectangle
            grpObject.DrawRectangle(objmyPen, 0, 0, (float)rndX, (float)rndY);
            drawnstr = "Rectangle ";
            break;
        case 2:                             // fill rectangle
            grpObject.FillRectangle(myBrush, 0, 0, (float)rndX, (float)rndY);
            drawnstr = "Filled rectangle to ";
            break;
        case 3:                             // draw ellipse
            grpObject.DrawEllipse(objmyPen, 0, 0, (float)rndX, (float)rndY);
            drawnstr = "Ellipse to ";
            break;
        case 4:                             // fill ellipse
            grpObject.FillEllipse(myBrush, 0, 0, (float)rndX, (float)rndY);
            drawnstr = "Filled ellipse to ";
            break;
        case 5:                             // draw square x = y
            grpObject.DrawRectangle(objmyPen, 0, 0, (float)rndX, (float)rndX);
            drawnstr = "Square to ";
            break;
        case 6:                             // draw circle x = y
            grpObject.DrawEllipse(objmyPen, 0, 0, (float)rndX, (float)rndX);
            drawnstr = "Circle to ";
            break;
    } // end switch

    // draw string
    grpObject.DrawString((drawnstr + rndX + "," + rndY),
```

```
        arial, myBrush, 0, 100);
    base.OnPaint(e);   // call form's paint event
}
```

3. Drawing Polygons

Let us study a filled polygon example. In this example the polygon is drawn as the user clicks on a panel. The mouse X and Y coordinates are added to an ArrayList and the panel is invalidated to force a redraw. Refer to Chapter 5, Arrays and Strings, for more details of the ArrayList.

Start a new project and place a panel on the form. We shall draw the polygon on the panel. Place a button labeled 'Reset' on the form.

Add the following code for the panel's mouseDown event, the paint event and the button click event, so the complete code is as follows:

```
namespace Polygon
{
    public partial class Form1 : Form
    {
        public Form1()
        {
            InitializeComponent();
        }

        private System.Collections.ArrayList aryPoints =
            new System.Collections.ArrayList();
        SolidBrush myBrush = new SolidBrush(Color.Gold);

        private void panel1_MouseDown(object sender, MouseEventArgs e)
        {
            aryPoints.Add(new Point(e.X, e.Y));
            // x and y postion of mouse passed
            panel1.Invalidate();
            // Invalidate to call panel's paint event
        }

        private void panel1_Paint(object sender, PaintEventArgs e)
        {
            Graphics myGrpObject = e.Graphics;
            // get panel's graphics object
            if (aryPoints.Count > 1)
            // 2 points or more - draw shape
            {
                Point[ ] arrayofPoints =
```

```
                    (Point[ ])aryPoints.ToArray(aryPoints[0].GetType( ));
                myGrpObject.FillPolygon(myBrush, arrayofPoints);
            }

        }// end method paint

        private void btnReset_Click(object sender, EventArgs e)
        {
            // create a new arrayList
            aryPoints = new System.Collections.ArrayList();
            panel1.Invalidate( );
            // and make sure paint is called
        }
    }
}
```

This may need a short explanation. An ArrayList (aryPoints) and brush are created with the line:

```
System.Collections.ArrayList aryPoints = new System.Collections.ArrayList();
```

When the mouse button is clicked, the mouse X and Y points are added to the dynamic arraylist (aryPoints). The X and Y position of the mouse is passed with the MouseEventArgs (e) and obtained from e.X and e.Y. The panel is invalidated, which causes it to be repainted by calling the panel's paint event.

The panel's paint event draws a filled polygon if there are more than 2 points. The FillPolygon method fills a polygon defined by an array of Points, so the ArrayList has to be converted to an array. This is done with the line of code:

```
 Point[ ] arrayofPoints = (Point[ ])aryPoints.ToArray(aryPoints[0].GetType( ));
```

The ArrayList can hold different types of data, so GetType is used to pass that information to the arrayofPoints array.

Finally when the Reset button is clicked a new ArrayList is created and the panel invalidated creating a new blank panel.

Your program should produce a display similar to figure 10.5 when the form is clicked:

4. A Scribble program.

Write a program that draws a line which follows the mouse movement. Hint: you will have to use the mousemove event.

10.14 Summary

In this chapter we have seen how to draw graphics. We have seen how to use the pen and brush to draw lines and basic shapes such as ellipse and rectangle, as well as more complicated shapes such as arcs, pie and filled pie. We have seen how the Paint method works and how to override the Paint method to ensure our drawings are always redrawn. Finally we have seen how we can add multimedia controls to our programs.

Chapter 11 - Debugging

11.1 Introduction

Sooner or later your programs will have a problem that causes a run-time error, hangs the computer, or just fails to work. I expect that has already happened to you by now. You will need to debug the program to find out why it's not working. The development environment has tools to help you debug your program and get it working. It should be noted however that the debug features are different between the Express and Professional versions.

The compiler will detect syntax errors and anything else it can't understand and it does go a long way to ensuring the program will remove many errors so that it will compile, but your program may still fail due to a run-time or logic error. Typical run-time errors are: divide by zero, text box type conversion error, or opening a non-existent file. We have seen how to trap run-time exceptions using try and catch code, but in this chapter we shall study how to use the debugger within the development environment.

11.2 Writing to the Debug Window

Before we start using the debugger, let's see how we can write a variable's value to the debug window using C# commands. We do this using the Debug.WriteLine method which is held in the System.Diagnostics namespace.

Start a new project and place a textbox and a button on the form. Set the text box's multiline property to true and add some text to the box (e.g. 'line 1', 'line 2' etc.). We shall display this in the debug output window.

Change the button click code to the following:

```
private void button1_Click(object sender, EventArgs e)
{
    // Create a string array and save the content of the lines.
    string[ ] tempArray = textBox1.Lines;

    // Loop through the array and write the array to the debug window.
    for (int count = 0; count < tempArray.Length; count++)
    {
        System.Diagnostics.Debug.WriteLine(tempArray[count]);
    }
}
```

Run the program. The following should appear in the debug window (see figure 11.1). If the Output window isn't displayed, click Debug>Windows>Output.

```
Output
Show output from:  Debug                                            ▼  📄  ↓
  '11.1DebugWindow.vshost.exe' (Managed (v4.0.30319)): Loaded 'C:\
  line1
  line2
  third line
  last line
  The thread '<No Name>' (0xf04) has exited with code 0 (0x0).
```

Figure 11.1 The Debug Window Output

Instead of adding code to display your variable's values in the Debug Window, you can display them by using the development environment's debug features.

11.3 Using the Debugger

The debugger provides options to:

- Run the program to the cursor position or specified points (known as a breakpoint).
- To view, disable, enable and delete breakpoints.
- To set conditions on breakpoint operation.
- To pause the program.
- To restart in different ways after meeting a breakpoint or pause.
- To view, evaluate and modify variables.

11.3.1 Setting a breakpoint

If you want to run the program to a specific point, you can run to the cursor position or set a breakpoint. To run to the cursor, right-click the line you want to stop at and select 'run to cursor'. Alternatively, you can set as many breakpoints as you want by clicking the grey area to the left of the line of code where you want the breakpoint. A red circle is displayed and the line of code highlighted, see figure 11.2. The breakpoint is removed if the red circle is clicked a second time.

```
private void button1_Click(object sender, EventArgs e)
{
    // Create a string array and save the content of the
    string[] tempArray = textBox1.Lines;
```

Figure 11.2 Setting a breakpoint

The program will stop when it reaches the breakpoint and the line of code about to be executed is highlighted in yellow, with an arrow pointing it. If the cursor is now hovered over a variable its value will be displayed, see figure 11.3.

```
// Create a string array and save the content of the l:
string[] tempArray = textBox1.Lines;
                        ⊞ 🖉 textBox1 {Text = "line1\r\nline2
// Loop through the array and write the array to the de
for (int count = 0; count < tempArray.length; count++)
```

Figure 11.3 Program stopped at breakpoint and displaying a value.

If the item is an object (as it is in figure 11.3), you can also expand its detail ('drill down') by holding the cursor over the object and then moving to the plus symbol. Figure 11.4 shows the textBox object expanded to show its properties. You can drill down further if items have a plus symbol (e.g. AutoCompleteCustomSource).

```
= textBox1.Lines;
              ⊟ 🖉 textBox1  {Text = "line1\r\nline2\r\nthird line\r\nlast line"}  ⊕
  array and ⊞ ● base {System.Windows.Forms.TextBoxBase}    {Text = "line1\r\nline2\r\nthird line\r\nlast line"}
  count < t     📷 AcceptsReturn                            false
            ⊞ 📷 AutoCompleteCustomSource                   {System.Windows.Forms.AutoCompleteStringCollection}
              📷 AutoCompleteMode                           None
              📷 AutoCompleteSource                         None
              📷 CharacterCasing                            Normal
              📷 Multiline                                  true
ged (v4.0.3   📷 PasswordChar                               0 '\0'
```

Figure 11.4 Displaying expanding object items

Note that you will have to completely stop the program running if you want to use the editor and make any changes to your program.

Now the program is paused, you can inspect your program variables; run the program at full speed (press the F5 key) or a line at a time (press F10 or F11). You can also change which line of code is to be executed next by dragging the yellow arrow to that line, but heed the warning! You can select these options from the debug toolbar, see figure 11.5. This appears when the program runs, but if it isn't displayed, choose View>Toolbars>Debug.

Figure 11.5. The Debug Toolbar

The toolbar icons from left to right are:
- start debugging (shortcut: F5)
- pause, or break all (ctrl + alt + break)
- stop debugging (shift + F5)
- restart, (ctrl + shift + F5)
- show next statement, (alt + Num *)
- step into, (F11)
- step over, (F10)

- step out, (shift + F11)
- toggle Hex display and
- display the breakpoint windows (output, locals, watch, immediate and stack).

Breakpoints can be set before or at run-time, but they must be on executable code; you cannot set a breakpoint at a comment. You can switch them on and off with the F9 key. Remember, you can also disable and re-enable a breakpoint by right-clicking the red circle.

11.3.2 Pausing the Program

The program can be paused by using the pause button on the toolbar, when the line of code which about to be executed will be displayed.

11.4 Conditional Breakpoints

If your breakpoint is in a loop, you may not want to break every time around the loop. With the Professional version of Visual Studio you can set breakpoints on a number of passes through a breakpoint, or when a variable has a certain value. You can set the conditions by right-clicking the red circle, see figure 11.6.

Figure 11.6 Breakpoint conditions

The conditions are:
- Location – when the program reaches a line and character location in a file (this doesn't have to be the current code file)
- Condition – the breakpoint is executed if the condition is true or has changed.
- Hit Count – the breakpoint is executed of the hit count is 1: always; 2: equal to, 3: multiple of, or 4: greater than or equal to
- Filter – you can filter out certain conditions, e.g. if thread or process ID = 12
- When hit – Print a message, or run a macro (mini program)

You can't do all of these with the Express edition, but you can add conditional or hit counts by adding extra code to do that for you, e.g.:

```
if ((loopCounter = 34) && (variable =123))
```

```
{
    count = count++;   // set breakpoint here
}
```

Remember, there has to be an executable line in the 'if' statement so that you can set a breakpoint. Adding this code will affect the timing of the loop, but that's unlikely to be a problem during debugging.

11.5 Restarting - Stepping code

To step the program a line at a time use 'Step Into' or 'Step Over'. Step Into (F11) steps the program a line at a time including any method calls. Step Over (F10) steps the program a line at a time, but runs any methods at full speed (unless they contain a breakpoint) and pauses at the line after the method call. You can also use Step Out, which takes you out of any methods you are debugging.

To use the Step Into, Step Over or Step Out commands press F11, F10 or Shift+F11, or click the icons on the debug toolbar, see figure 11.7

Figure 11.7 Restart option icons

11.6 The breakpoint windows

We have already seen the breakpoint output window where we can display variable values. The other windows you can select from the drop-down box are Local, Watch, Immediate and Call Stack.

11.6.1. Local window

This will display the local variables, see figure 11.8

Locals

Name	Value		Type
⊞ ● this	{_11._1DebugWindow.Form1, Text: Debug window output}		_11._1DebugWindow.Form1
⊞ ● sender	{Text = "Show debug data"}		object {System.Windows.Forms.Button}
⊟ ● e	{X = 88 Y = 13 Button = Left}		System.EventArgs {System.Windows.Forms.MouseEve
⊞ ● [System.Window	{X = 88 Y = 13 Button = Left}		System.Windows.Forms.MouseEventArgs
⊞ ⚙ Static members			
● count	1		int
⊟ ● tempArray	{string[4]}		string[]
● [0]	"line1"	🔍 ▾	string
● [1]	"line2"	🔍 ▾	string
● [2]	"third line"	🔍 ▾	string
● [3]	"last line"	🔍 ▾	string

Figure 11.8 The Debug Local window

In this example the window is showing all the parameters available to this method:

'this' - the current object (Form1);
'sender' – the button that called the method (and it's text 'Show Debug Data';
'e' - the sender's arguments (in this case the mouse position X, Y and left-click);
'count' – an integer variable with the value 1;
'tempArray' – a string array. This has been expanded to see the contents.

11.6.2 Watch window

This is used to examine variables and is enabled when the program is at a breakpoint. The variables or expressions to be watched are set by entering them in the name field, see figure 11.9.

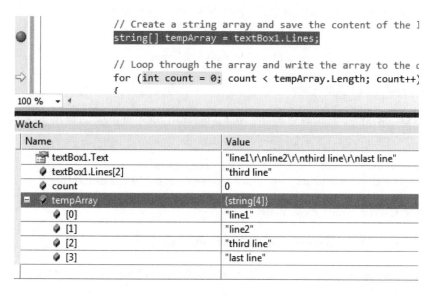

Figure 11.9 The Debug Watch window

In this example, quite a few items are being watched, including textBox1.Text, textBox1.Lines[2], count and tempArray. Remember, if an item is not declared within this block of code, its value cannot be displayed.

11.6.3. The Immediate window.

This window lets you type in an expression to evaluate, see figure 11.10.

```
Immediate Window
number1*number2/Math.Sin(0.2)
142860.50034203648
```

Figure 11.10 The Debug Immediate window

Figure 11.10 The Debug Immediate window

Note that you can use the Math class in this. You can also use this window to assign values and then continue debugging.

11.6.4. The Call Stack.

This window lists the calls that were executed to get to the current code position. It can be useful to find out how your program got where it is. Figure 11.11 shows the current location came from button1_Click, which came from the Main() code, line 18.

Call Stack
Name
→ 11.1DebugWindow.exe!_11._1DebugWindow.Form1.button1_Click(object sender, System.EventArgs e) Line 27
[External Code]
11.1DebugWindow.exe!_11._1DebugWindow.Program.Main() Line 18 + 0x1d bytes
[External Code]

Figure 11.11 The Call Stack window

11.7 Self Assessment Exercises

You will get plenty of chances to debug your programs! But you might like to try some of the following:

1. Watch the video #5 'How do I step the debugger' at:
   http://msdn.microsoft.com/en-gb/vcsharp/bb798022.aspx#VSIDE

2. Use the run to cursor command.

3. If your version supports it, try the breakpoint conditions.

4. Once stopped at a breakpoint, examine variables and know how to 'drill down into objects.

5. Step through your code using Step Into, Step Over and Step Out.

6. Use all the breakpoint windows.

11.8 Summary

We have covered how to use the debugger to correct your program errors. You can run the program to the cursor or a breakpoint. You can set, view, edit, enable and disable breakpoints. The debug windows help you view, evaluate and modify data and show the stack providing information on the calls that have been executed.

You can find out more on debugging by entering 'debugging [C#]'in the help search box.

Chapter 12 - Threading

12.1 Introduction

So far our programs have been running a single program or task at a time. You can split some programs into separate tasks called threads and run these tasks at the same time (concurrently) and for the threads to communicate with each other. Threading can speed up programs that use different resources such as files and networking, but at the same time may create resource sharing problems. Threads can be run on different processors in multiple processor chips. As we will see in the next chapter we will use threads to perform networking tasks.

12.2 Threads

You can split your program into individual tasks, or threads. The .NET environment allows concurrent programming by controlling the execution of the threads.

Each thread is allocated a priority and runs either until it finishes, runs out of its allocated time, or is held up for some reason (e.g. waiting for some data, say from the internet or another thread). This operation is controlled by the operating system. You do not need a modern threading processor to run threaded programs.

Threads move between states. The thread states are:

- Unstarted – created, but waiting for Start
- Started – wait for Run
- Running – it runs when a processor is assigned to it (dispatched)
- Stopped – Thread is terminated or aborted
- Blocked – when making I/O request, waits for I/O
- WaitSleepJoin
    - Waiting for something else to happen (e.g. other code to complete)
    - Sleep for a specific time
    - Join (waiting for another thread to terminate)
- Suspend – a method call; goes to Started on Resume

A simplified flow diagram of a threaded program is shown in figure 12.1

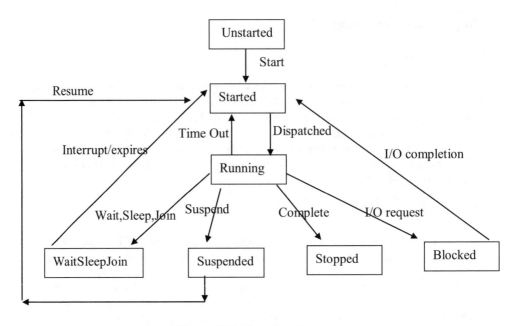

Figure 12.1 Thread states

12.3 Writing Thread Code

As you might expect the thread code is written as a class and a Thread object is instantiated the same way as any other object. Once a thread class is written, you can then instantiate and start as many threads as you want, just like you do with objects.

Threading code needs the System.Threading namespace (using System.Threading;) added to your code.

The thread code is in its own class, which can have its own methods. It is defined just like a class e.g.

```
Class MyThreadCode {
// declarations
public MyThreadCode ( )
  {
  // constructor
  }
private myThreadMethods ( )
  {
  // methods go here
  }
} // end of thread code
```

The main code instantiates and starts the thread using ThreadStart as follows:

```
MyThreadCode myThread = new MyThreadCode();
Thread thread1 =
    new Thread (new ThreadStart ( MyThreadCode.StartMethod ));
```

ThreadStart is a delegate - an object that refers to a method and is used to call the method. It's like a pointer which allows a third-party access to a method. We won't go into any more detail, just use the code provided.

The thread's properties can be accessed if necessary, e.g:

```
thread1.Name = "first Thread";
```

And then the thread can be started:

```
thread1.Start();
```

12.4 Thread sleeping example

Let's explain this with an example. Let's start by writing a thread that puts itself to sleep for a random amount of time and when it wakes up displays its name. We will later run as many of these threads as we want.

Start a new project and call it ThreadSleepExample.

Add a new class (Project > Add Class) and call it 'MySleepThread'

Add 'using System.Threading;' at the top of the thread class code, and type in the following code for the MySleepThread class:

```
namespace ThreadSleepExample
{
  class MySleepThread
  {
    // private declarations for each thread
    private int sleepTime;
    private static Random random = new Random( );

    // constructor

    public MySleepThread( )
    {
      sleepTime = random.Next(10000);      // random time to 10s
    }
```

```
// Thread method
// - displays name, sleeps and when woken, displays 'awake'
public void MySleepMethod()
{
    // get a reference to the current Thread
    Thread current = Thread.CurrentThread;
    // display message – sleeping for threadSleep time
    System.Diagnostics.Debug.WriteLine
            (current.Name + " sleeping for " + sleepTime);

    // Sleep
    Thread.Sleep(sleepTime);

    // Wake up ! -  display message
    System.Diagnostics.Debug.WriteLine(current.Name + " awake !");
}
} // end ThreadCode
} // end namespace ThreadSleepExample
```

Note that the program writes to the console debug window, so this needs to be displayed if you want to see the output from the program. (Display with Debug > Windows > Output). If the program had used MessageBox.Show to display its output, the program would wait for input from the user, which isn't what we want. You could also write this as a console application.

As you can imagine, if there are multiple threads all trying to write to the same label or textbox to display their information, there can be a problem.

This thread needs to be instantiated and started. We shall do this when the form loads. Try the following code for the form load event:

```
private void Form1_Load(object sender, EventArgs e)
{
    // Display message
    MessageBox.Show("Thread will start when OK is pressed");

    // Instantiate MySleepThread – run constructor code, get random time
    MySleepThread sleepThread = new MySleepThread();

    // Instantiate thread with method to run
    Thread thread1 = new Thread
        (new ThreadStart (sleepThread.MySleepMethod));

    // We can now refer to thread
    thread1.Name = "first Thread";
```

```
        // and finally start the thread
        thread1.Start();
    }
```

Run the program. The Debug output window will be similar to figure 12.2:

```
first Thread sleeping for 44
first Thread awake !
The thread 'first Thread' (0x1010) has exited with code 0
(0x0).
```

Figure 12.2 Thread output

Incidentally, if you see a message like 'The thread '<No Name>' (0x6e8) has exited with code 0 (0x0).' this is nothing to do with your thread. It occurs occasionally and I believe it's the thread that deals with the managed .NET environment code.

As you will see the although the thread is terminated, but the form is still active. You can use Application.Exit() to close all the threads and windows.

The other point to note is that the

12.5 Multiple Threading example

Now that we have some idea how threads start and run, let's expand the previous example to run multiple threads. We will simply change the form load code to create threads on a button click.

Repeat the above exercise. This time, instead of writing the form load code, add a button to the form. This time we will add a count to identify each thread. Add the following count declaration before 'public Form1 ( )'.

```
    int count = 0;
```

Don't forget to add 'using System.Threading;' to the code and type the following code for the button click:

```
    private void button1_Click(object sender, EventArgs e)
    {
        count++;              // unique value for each thread
        MySleepThread sleepThread = new MySleepThread();
        Thread thread1 = new Thread
              (new ThreadStart(sleepThread.MySleepMethod));
        thread1.Name = "Thread " + count.ToString();
        thread1.Start();      // and finally start the thread
```

```
}
```

Run the program and click the button quickly a few times to run several threads. The output should be similar to figure 12.3:

```
Thread 1 sleeping for 7531
Thread 2 sleeping for 7077
Thread 3 sleeping for 4464
Thread 4 sleeping for 5339
Thread 3 awake !
The thread 'Thread 3' (0xf1c) has exited with code 0 (0x0).
Thread 4 awake !
The thread 'Thread 4' (0x1204) has exited with code 0
(0x0).
Thread 2 awake !
The thread 'Thread 2' (0x131c) has exited with code 0
(0x0).
Thread 1 awake !
The thread 'Thread 1' (0x580) has exited with code 0 (0x0).
```

Figure 12.3 Multiple thread output

Note that the threads run and put themselves to sleep for different lengths of time. Each thread has its own value for count which is displayed.

You have created a multi-tasking, concurrent program environment. We will not go into any more detail, for instance cover communication between threads, here.

12.6 Accessing form controls from threads

You might get a situation where you want your thread to access a control such as a TextBox on a form. If you try to do this from a thread, you will get a 'cross-thread error' at run-time.

You cannot access an object owned by one thread from another thread. You program has to request that the owning thread do the work for you and to do so you call the control's invoke method (Control.Invoke) and pass it the data needed.

There are two ways to solve this problem.

1. In File Load event, add the code to ignore the error:

    CheckForIllegalCrossThreadCalls = false;

    But this isn't really good programming.

2. Provide the correct coding checks and call the Invoke method. We shall do this. If you really want to find out more about how Invoke works, you can refer to the Microsoft web site.

Start a New Project and add a button and a TextBox on the form. Set the Multiline property 'true'. We will write a new thread that will write to this text box.
Add the using statements and declare the count variable before 'public Form1 ( )' as before:

```
int count = 0;
```

For the button click add the following code:

```
private void button1_Click(object sender, EventArgs e)
{
    count++;
    // use 'this' to pass a reference to this form
    MySleepThread sleepThread = new MySleepThread(this);
    Thread thread1 = new Thread
            (new ThreadStart(sleepThread.MySleepMethod));
    thread1.Name = "Thread " + count.ToString();
    thread1.Start();      // and finally start the thread
}
```

Note that this time we have used 'this' to pass a reference to the form from the thread.

We will now add the Invoke method so that we can write to the textbox from the thread.

Before public Form1 () add the delegate declaration.

```
delegate void SetTextCallBack(string text);
```

Add code to display on list box using cross threaded code, say before private void button1_Click:

```
public void WriteToTextBox(string strText)
{
    // InvokeRequired compares the thread ID of the
    // calling thread to the thread ID of the creating thread.
    // if different, it calls Invoke (when it will be the same).

    if (this.textBox1.InvokeRequired)
    {
        SetTextCallBack d = new SetTextCallBack(WriteToTextBox);
        this.Invoke(d, new Object[ ] { strText } );
    }
```

```
        else // it's OK  - add text to text box
        {
            this.textBox1.Text += strText;
        }
    } //end WriteToTextBox
```

Add a new class (MyWriteThread) and type the following code:

```
class MyWriteThread
{
    // declarations
    private int sleepTime;
    private static Random random = new Random();
    private Form1 f;                          // Reference to Form1

    // constructor
    public MyWriteThread(Form1 f)
    {
        sleepTime = random.Next(10000);  // random time to 10 s
        this.f = f;                          // Assign a reference to form1
    }

    // Thread method
    public void MySleepMethod()
    {                                         // get reference to current Thread
        Thread current = Thread.CurrentThread;
        Thread.Sleep(sleepTime);              // Sleep
        // Wake up ! -  display message on text box
        f.WriteToTextBox(current.Name + " awake !\r\n");
        // f is reference to form1
    }
}          // end ThreadCode
```

Run the program. The output should be similar to figure 12.4.

Figure 12.4 Accessing form controls

You should terminate your threads when you have finished with them. The easiest way to do this is to use the Abort() method. This begins the process of terminating the thread, and usually terminates it. For example use:

```
thread1.Abort();
```

12.7 Other thread considerations

We have only touched on threading here, for instance we haven't seen how to pass data between threads. Also there can be problems running threaded programs; not least of all that high priority threads can starve low priority ones and threads may hang waiting on each other. This is without mentioning synchronization, thread communication and using buffers, but we have covered the basics here. This will be enough for us to deal with internet communications in the next chapter.

12.8 Self Assessment Exercises

1. Change the code in 12.4 so that it uses MessageBox.Show() rather than write to the debug output window and see what happens.

2. Write Invoke code to write to other controls, say a listbox or label.

3. Find out more about delegates

4. Find out how to pass data and communicate between threads.

12.9 Summary

This has been a brief introduction to threaded programs. We have seen why we need threaded programs. We have seen the various states a thread can take and how they move from one state to another. We have seen how to write a threaded program and how to put them to sleep. We have run a multi-threaded program, each of which can access the same form control to report its progress. We have also mentioned possible problems with threaded programs. All of this provides the background for internet communications that we will cover next.

Chapter 13 - Internet Applications

13.1 Introduction

Now that we have some idea about how we use threads to run sections of our program concurrently, we can see how to apply that to an internet application. In this chapter we will write internet communication programs using threads that will wait for data to be received from the internet and at the same time be able to send data to the internet. Without threads the programs would hang waiting for data to be received. We shall look at programs using the internet communication protocols Transmission Control Protocol (TCP) and User Datagram Protocol (UDP). We will end up with an internet chat program.

13.2 Client-Server communication

We will start by looking at client-server internet communication. In this case the client (e.g. a user typing a web request) sends a request to a server which responds with the data. This response could be an HTML page, a file transfer, an ASP.NET page request or many other communications. Initially we will look at a TCP server application that receives data and then expand this to respond with data. We will then study a TCP client application which sends data and finally to display the server's response. Having produced this TCP communication program, we will write a similar program using UDP protocols.

Networking capabilities are provided through the System.Net.Sockets namespace. There are no controls to be placed on the form. The communication sockets are created at run-time.

13.3 TCP and UDP

The two main protocols used by the internet are TCP (Transmission Control Protocol) and UDP (User Datagram Protocol). The main difference is that TCP implements a connection and re-transmissions whereas the UDP protocol just sends data in packets and doesn't care if they are received. UDP is useful in streaming technology when re-transmission is irrelevant.

TCP communication is based on streaming (similar to streaming we saw with disk I/O). A process or program establishes a connection to another process and data transfers occur in continuous streams. The alternative UDP communication uses packet based transmissions known as datagram sockets. This protocol is a connectionless service in which packets are sent and can arrive in any order. This requires more programming, but may result in a faster performance.

We shall start with TCP communications and as our server will wait for connections and client requests we will use threads. If you are unsure about these read the chapter on threads again.

13.4 Creating a TCP server.

A TCP server simply listens on the internet at a port and at the computer's IP address. There are five steps to creating a TCP streaming server:

1. Create a server using a TCPListener with the code which sets up the IP and port addresses. A TCPListener object is created with the following code:

```
Int32 port = 5000;
IPAddress localAddr = IPAddress.Parse("127.0.0.1");
TcpListener server = new TcpListener(localAddr, port);
```

The program 'listens' at the port number and the computer's IP (Internet Protocol) address. Port values below 1204 are reserved. The IP address 127.0.0.1 or "localhost" refers to the host computer, so you can run the client and server applications on any PC and you don't need to know or change the IP address for different PCs.

2. Start listening at the port. The TcpListener we called 'server' is started with the command:

```
server.Start( );
```

The server simply listens at this address. The server creates a connection to the client when a client request is received via a socket.

3. Establish the connection between client and server. To start the TCPListener, use the code:

```
Socket connection= server.AcceptSocket( );
```

Socket is defined in the System.Net.Sockets namespace so at the top of your code you will need to add:

```
using System.Net.Sockets;
```

4. Communicate with the client. Create the network stream and use the Socket methods Send( ) and Receive( ). We also create BinaryReader and BinaryWriter, read and write objects. By contrast the UDP communications use SendTo( ) and ReceiveFrom( ) methods.

5. Terminate the connection. Use the Socket method Close( ).

13.5 Threads

As we have said, without threads the program would hang waiting for data to be received. We will put the Receive method into a thread allowing other sections of our program to run; the thread will continue when data is received. We shall see how this all works in the following example. Remember if we want to write to a textbox or other control from a thread we will have to deal with cross-thread exceptions.

13.6 Creating a TCP client

The TcpClient makes the connection to the server at the PCs port and IP address. Four steps have to be taken to create a TCP client:

1. Create a TcpClient client and connect to the server using the code:

   ```
   TcpClient client = new TcpClient();
   Client.connect (serverAddress, serverPort);
   ```

The Client code will connect to a server, so the **serverAddress** is either the IP address of the server of type 'IPAddress' (e.g. 127.0.0.1, see above) or a string containing its name (e.g. "localhost"). The **serverPort** is the port number of the server, i.e. the one we used when we created the server. To run code on your PC, use the local IP address 127.0.0.1 or "localhost", otherwise you will need to know the IP address of your computer. You can find this in Control Panel or you can run the MSDOS command 'ipconfig'. It's a number like 192.123.456.7.

2. Create the network stream using the **TcpClient getStream( )** method.
3. Communicate with the server using the NetworkStream methods **Read( )**, **ReadByte( )**, **Write( )** or **WriteByte( )**.
4. Finally close the connection using the method **Close( )**.

13.7 TCP Client-Server application

We shall develop a program with a TCP server that receives and echoes data sent to it and then add a TCP client that sends data to the server and displays the data returned. We could extend this so the server does some useful work such as squaring any numbers sent to it, or retrieving data from a file.

Start a new application and call it Server. On the form place a list box (called lstRxdData) and buttons to listen and disconnect (btnListen and btnDisconnect). Your GUI should look similar to Figure 13.1.

Figure 13.1. Server application

At the following to the using statements at the top of the code:

```
using System.Net.Sockets;
using System.Net;
using System.IO;
using System.Threading;
```

Before the code public Form () add the declarations:

```
private Socket connection;
private NetworkStream socketStream;
private BinaryReader reader;
private BinaryWriter writer;
```

Add the following method:

```
public void RunServer()
{
    try         //   and catch (Exception error)
    {
        // create listener
        Int32 port = 5000;
        IPAddress localAddr = IPAddress.Parse("127.0.0.1");
        TcpListener server = new TcpListener(localAddr, port);
          // defined in System.Net.Sockets

        server.Start( );         // start listening

        // establish and accept connection
        connection = server.AcceptSocket( );
```

175

```
// Create a NetworkStream for the socket
socketStream = new NetworkStream(connection);

//create read and write objects to send data through stream
writer = new BinaryWriter(socketStream);
reader = new BinaryReader(socketStream);

// display on listBox this will cross thread error
lstRxdData.Items.Add("connection made");

// and tell client
writer.Write("Message from Server: connected OK");

// now loop reading and displaying data received

string msgFromClient = null;
do
{
  try
  {

    // read the string sent by client and terminate if QUIT
    msgFromClient = reader.ReadString();

    lstRxdData.Items.Add(msgFromClient);
    // won't hang because it'll be in a thread

  // and echo data
    writer.Write(msgFromClient);

  } // end try
    catch (Exception)
  {
    break;
  } // catch
}
while (msgFromClient != "QUIT");     // close if QUIT received

lstRxdData.Items.Add("Client disconnected");

// and close connection
reader.Close();
writer.Close();
socketStream.Close();
connection.Close();
Application.Exit();     // and close app and threads
```

```
    } // end try
    catch (Exception error)
    {
      MessageBox.Show(error.ToString());
    } // catch

  } // end RunServer
```

RunServer will be run as a thread.

For the listen button click we are going to instantiate and start the RunServer thread code:

1. If it isn't present, add the using statement: using System.Threading;
2. Add the private declaration: private Thread serverThread;
3. Change the code for the listen button click to:

```
private void btnListen_Click(object sender, EventArgs e)
{
   serverThread = new Thread(new ThreadStart(RunServer));
   serverThread.Start();
   btnListen.Enabled = false;
}
```

Add the code for disconnect button:

```
private void btnDisconnect_Click(object sender, EventArgs e)
{
   try
   {
     if (connection.Connected)
     {
        reader.Close();
        writer.Close();
        socketStream.Close();
        connection.Close();
        btnDisconnect.Enabled = false;
        serverThread.Abort();        // and terminate the thread
     }
   } // try
   catch (Exception error)
   {
      MessageBox.Show(error.ToString());
   } // catch
}
```

.NET security won't let a thread write directly to a control on the form, (you get illegal cross thread error) so to make life easy, add this line to the Form_load( ) event:

```
CheckForIllegalCrossThreadCalls = false;
```

If you want to do it the correct way, see the chapter on threads and use the Invoke method.

Check the code runs. You will get an error on disconnecting because a connection hasn't been made by a client. Save and close the project. We now create a TCP client that sends data to the server.

13.8 TCP Client Code

We will now create a second application which will act as a TCP client. Both this and the TCP server can be tested on the same PC.

1. Create a form as before with listbox (lstRxdData) and buttons (btnConnect and btnDisconnect), this time call the button 'Connect, rather than 'Listen'
    Now add a textbox (txtSendData).

    The design should be similar to figure 13.2

2. Add the using statements as before (IO, Net, Net.Sockets and Threading)
3. Add the private declarations as follows:

    ```
    private NetworkStream clientStream;
    private BinaryReader reader;
    private BinaryWriter writer;
    private Thread clientThread;
    private string message = null;
    ```

4. Now add the client code and thread code:

```
public void RunClient()
{
  TcpClient client;
  // init tcpClient
  try
  {
    // 1. Create client and connect to server- give
    client = new TcpClient();

    // give IP address and port to talk to
    client.Connect("localhost", 5000);
```

```
// get network stream
clientStream = client.GetStream();

// create read and write objects
writer = new BinaryWriter(clientStream);
reader = new BinaryReader(clientStream);
lstRxdData.Items.Add("connecting to server");

// we will ignore cross-thread errors in form load,

   do
      try
      {
         // read message from server until QUIT received
         message = reader.ReadString();
         lstRxdData.Items.Add(message);
      } // try
      catch (Exception error)
      {
         MessageBox.Show("Error reading from server "+error.ToString());
      } // catch
   while (message != "QUIT");
   // close connection
   lstRxdData.Items.Add("Closing connection");
   writer.Close();
   reader.Close();
   clientStream.Close();
   client.Close();
   Application.Exit();     // and close app and threads

   } // end try
   catch (Exception error)
   {
      MessageBox.Show("Error creating connection " + error.ToString());
   }

} // end runclient
```

5. To start the thread when the connect button is clicked, change the button click code to following:

```
private void btnConnect_Click(object sender, EventArgs e)
{
   clientThread = new Thread(new ThreadStart(RunClient));
   clientThread.Start();
   btnConnect.Enabled = false;
```

```
        }
```

6. Let's ignore cross-thread errors. Add this line to the Form_load( ) event:

```
CheckForIllegalCrossThreadCalls = false;
```

7. Finally add the code for the KeyDown event to send data when enter is pressed in text box:

```
private void txtSendData_KeyDown(object sender, KeyEventArgs e)
{
   if (e.KeyCode == Keys.Enter)
   {
      // when enter key pressed, write to writer (binaryWriter to ClientStream)
      writer.Write(txtSendData.Text);
      // and clear text box
      txtSendData.Clear();
   }
}
```

Run this client code from the Visual Studio environment and the previous server .EXE code from its bin>Debug folder.

Press Listen to start the server listening and press Connect on the Client. You may be trapped out by your firewall, but the server should display the message 'connection made' and the client the message: 'connecting to server' and 'Message from Server: connected OK'

You can now type messages in the client and they are echoed back. Your program displays should be similar to figure 13.2.

Figure 13.2 TCP Client and Server displays

Typing QUIT will close both programs. Without the Application.Exit(); code, the connection is closed but the thread still runs. You might like to try and see how to terminate the thread, so that re-connections can be made.

Note that we don't need to know the IP address because we have used 'localhost' as the IP address.

13.9 UDPClient communications - A chat program

Let's now design a communication program (a chat program) using the UDP protocols. This time we will use the UDPClient class. This both sends and receives; there is no Listener or Client class. This is different from the TCP example which had individual Server and Client applications.

We will start with one program that both sends and receives (to itself). Then we will modify this slightly and run two versions of this program that will chat to each other.

We shall use the UDPClient's Send and Receive methods to send and receive data. When we run the second copy of this program to make a chat program will just send to an IP address and port. We will see how the Receive method finds out the IPaddress and port of the sending PC, and consequently to reply to.

13.9.1 UDPClient.Send( )

The Send method sends a datagram packet. Its parameters are: a byte array containing the data, the number of bytes to be sent, the destination host name and port address.

The datagram packet to be sent is a byte array. This is created from a string using System.Text.Encoding's GetBytes method:

```
byte[ ] sendData = System.Text.Encoding.ASCII.GetBytes(string);
```

This will be sent to the server using the code:

```
client.Send(sendData, sendData.Length, "IPaddress", int.Parse("port"));
```

'IPaddress' and 'port' are the IP address and port of the destination computer.

13.9.2 UDPClient.Receive( )

The UDPClient.Receive method accepts a datagram packet. Our program will be put in a loop waiting to receive data and this is put in a thread so our program won't hang waiting for data. We will be able to send and receive at the same time.

The Receive method has one parameter, an IPEndpoint. The IPEndpoint is a combined IP address and port number of the remote host from which the data was sent. We can use this to send the data received back to the client using the Send method.

The Receive method returns the datagram packet received as a byte array. We shall use the following code to accept the data:

```
byte[ ] rxdata = client.Receive(ref this.rxPoint);
```

Note that the 'ref' keyword is used. This allows the Receive method to update and return the IPEndpoint, rxPoint, consequently we know where to respond. We will use rxPoint in the Send method.

13.9.3 UDP program threads

Let's try our UDP chat program. Remember, we will start with just one application which uses only UDPClient classes to both send and receive; I will call them 'client' and 'server'. The client will send data typed into a textbox to the server, the server will display this data and reply echoing the data back to the client. As both the server and client will have to wait for data there will be two threads, we'll call them WaitForDataFromClient and WaitForDataFromServer.

As we will see later, the client will send data via port 5000 to port 5001 on a KeyDown event; the server will listen for packets on port 5001, display the message and reply to the sending port, port 5000, when the client will display the echoed data.

The communication will be set up as shown in figure 13.3.

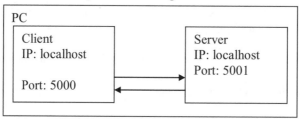

Figure 13.3 UDP Client - Server communications

Rather than ignoring IllegalCrossThread errors as we did previously, we shall correctly write from the threads to the list box display.

Initially we will run the application on our PC using the IP: 'localhost', but later we will run a second version of the program so a true chat will run. It could then be run on separate PCs, so long as the IP addresses are known.

13.9.4 UDP GUI design

Start a new project (UDPChat) and place a list box (lstRxdData) and a text box (txtData) on the form. The list box will display the data received. The text box will contain the data to be sent when the return key is pressed.

The IP and port values are declared at the start of the program. Port values less than 1024 are reserved; we will use 5000 and 5001.

Your interface should be similar to figure 13.4

Figure 13.4 UDP Chat application

We will start by writing the server thread code that waits for data from the client using the UDPClient.Receive method.

13.9.5 UDP server code

Add the following at the top of your code:
```
using System.Net;
using System.Net.Sockets;
using System.Threading;
```

We have to declare a UdpClient which be the server and create and start a thread which waits for data from the client and puts this in the list box.

Declare an UdpClient and an initial IPEndPoint for the server; this will be overwritten with the IPEndPoint of the client. Add the following code after the declaration: public partial class Form1 : Form {

```
// Server
UdpClient server = new UdpClient(5001);
IPEndPoint rxPoint = new IPEndPoint(new IPAddress(0), 0);

// add the thread call to allow us to write to the list box as well:
delegate void SetTextCallBack(string text);
```

Follow this with the method that waits for the data from the client:

```
// Server code
private void WaitForDataFromClient ()
{
    while (true)
    {
        // receive data from server
        byte[ ] ClientData = server.Receive(ref rxPoint);

        // display on list box
        ListBoxDisplay("Server received: " +
            (System.Text.Encoding.ASCII.GetString(ClientData)));

        // and echo back
        ListBoxDisplay("Sending back");
        server.Send(ClientData, ClientData.Length, rxPoint);
    } // end while true
} // end WaitForDataFromClient
```

To write to the list box from the thread add the following code after the code you have just entered:

```
    private void ListBoxDisplay(string message)
    {
        this.SetListBox(message);
    }

    private void SetListBox(string strText)
    {
      if (this.lstRxdData.InvokeRequired)
      {
        SetTextCallBack d = new SetTextCallBack(SetListBox);
        this.Invoke(d, new Object[ ]{strText});
      }
      else // it's OK
      {
        this.lstRxdData.Items.Add(strText);
      }
```

> }   //end SetListBox

We covered all this before in threading. Revisit that chapter if you need to.

Now we need to start the server's thread.
Add the following after InitializeComponent( );

```
// start server
Thread serverThread = new Thread
        (new ThreadStart(WaitForDataFromClient));
serverThread.Start();
```

You can now run the program to check it. You may have to give your firewall access to your program.

Now we need to declare the UdpClient 'client' and use the Send method to send the data.

Add the following code to declare the 'client' and endpoint after the 'UdpClient server' declaration:

```
UdpClient client = new UdpClient(5000);
IPEndPoint txPoint = new IPEndPoint(new IPAddress(0), 0);
```

Change the KeyDown event for the text box to the following:

```
private void txtData_KeyDown(object sender, KeyEventArgs e)
{
  if (e.KeyCode == Keys.Enter)
  {
      // create a string datagram packet
      string packet = txtData.Text;

      // convert packet to byte array
      byte[ ] sendData = System.Text.Encoding.ASCII.GetBytes(packet);

      // send to server on port 5001
      this.client.Send(sendData, sendData.Length, "localhost", 5001);
      // and clear text box
      txtData.Clear();
  }
}
```

Check the program runs. Your firewall may block your program, but you should be able to type into the text box and see the message 'Server received:' followed by the message in the list box.

Note that although the server code echoes the data using the server.Send code, it's not accepted by the client (yet) and there is no error message. That is what is expected by the UDP protocol. We'll write the code to accept the data now.

The thread that was started continues when you close the window. You will have to stop debugging to add further code. If you run the .EXE file the only way to stop the process is to use the Task Manager. If you want to, see if you can add code that terminates the thread.

13.9.6 UDP client code

Now we have to add the client code to accept the data echoed from the 'server'. This will be put in a thread so that the program won't hang. We have already declared the UDPClient object and transmit IPEndPoint for the client.

Add the thread code to wait for data sent by the server. This will echo the data sent by the server.

Add the following after the WaitForDataFromClient method:

```
private void WaitForDataFromServer()
{
   while (true)
   {
      // receive data from client
      byte[ ] rxdata = client.Receive(ref this.txPoint);
      // cross-thread exception if lstRxdData.Items.Add ( ) is used
      // so call
      ListBoxDisplay("Client received: " +
           System.Text.Encoding.ASCII.GetString(rxdata));
   }
} // end of wait for data
```

Declare and start the thread 'WaitForDataFromServer' which waits for data. Add the following code after InitializeComponent( );

```
Thread clientThread = new Thread(new ThreadStart
     (WaitForDataFromServer));
clientThread.Start( );
```

You can now run the program, data typed into the text box is sent to the 'server', echoed back and displayed by the 'client' on the list box, see figure 13.5

Figure 13.5 UDPChat Display

13.10 A Local Chat program

We can now try to run our program as a true chat program. We will run two copies of our chat program on the same PC. To do this we have to use 2 different ports. They will communicate as shown in figure 13.6. We can't run the same program twice, as they will both try to use the same port and an error would occur.

Figure 13.6 Remote chat program communications

Note:
Chat1 onKeyDown sends out (using Client.Send) via port 5001 to port 5678. Chat2 'server' receives this (on port 5678) and sends back to the rxPoint (5001). Chat1 receives this and displays 'Client received ..'
Chat2 onKeyDown sends out (using Client.Send) via port 5679 to port 5000 (Chat1 server code) which sends back to the rxPoint (5679). This is received by Chat2 (wait for data from server) and displays message in the listBox (Client received ..)

We will make a copy of our first program (Chat2), and change the port addresses for this to 5678 and 5679. We will also change the port address to which Chat1 writes to 5678.

Before creating the second chat program, return to your chat program and change the following line from:

```
this.client.Send(sendData, sendData.Length, "localhost", 5001);
```
to:
```
this.client.Send(sendData, sendData.Length, "localhost", 5678);
```

13.10.1 The Second Chat program

At this point, it's easiest to run a second Visual Studio application. Repeat the instructions for the first chat program. This time however change the server and client declarations for the second program as follows:

From:
```
UdpClient server = new UdpClient(5001);
```
to:
```
UdpClient server = new UdpClient(5678);
```

and from:
```
UdpClient client = new UdpClient(5000);
```
to:
```
UdpClient client = new UdpClient(5679);
```

Make sure the KeyDown event now sends to port 5001, as originally:

```
this.client.Send(sendData, sendData.Length, "localhost", 5001);
```

You can also display the rxPoint. In WaitForDataFromClient, change ListBoxDisplay code to:

```
ListBoxDisplay("Sending back to " + rxPoint.ToString()+"\n");
```

Compile and run both programs (or run the EXE files) and chat, see figure 13.7

Figure 13.7 Chat program displays

13.11 Remote Chat program

You can now try to the run the programs on separate PCs, as shown in figure 13.8. You can now have the same server and client port numbers, because the IP addresses are different.

Figure 13.8 Remote chat IP and port connections

You will have to find out your IP addresses and change the code, for example to:

this.client.Send(sendData, sendData.Length, "192.168.1.104", 5001);

You will also have to check your port addresses. I had the following IP and port addresses

	PC	Laptop
IP:	IP: 192.168.1.104	IP: 192.168.1.100
KeyDown sends to IP & port	192.168.1.100, 5001	192.168.1.104, 5001

189

| Server port | 5001 | 5001 |
| Client port | 5678 | 5678 |

The port to reply to is obtained from rxPoint in the server.Receive(ref rxPoint); code.

The resulting communication is shown in figure 13.9.

Figure 13.9 PC and Laptop displays

13.12 Finding your PC's IP address

The following code will display your PC's name and IP address:
You need to add 'using System.Net;' at the top of your code

```
string hostName = Dns.GetHostName();
MessageBox.Show ("Host Name = " + hostName);
IPHostEntry local = Dns.GetHostEntry(hostName);
foreach (IPAddress ipaddress in local.AddressList)
{
        MessageBox.Show("IPAddress = " + ipaddress.ToString());
}
```

13.13 Self Assessment Exercises

1. TCP Server:

Having created the first TCP client and server applications, make the server to do a useful task such as square a number sent to it. You will need to think about the data string you receive, how to check that it is a number and how to reply with either the square of the number or an error message.

2. Change the TCP server and client code so that it reads the IP and port address from text boxes.

Basically, the TcpListener will be instantiated as follows:

```
TcpListener server = new TcpListener
        (IPAddress.Parse(txtIp.Text), int.Parse(txtListenerPort.Text););
```

Change the client connect code to:

```
client.Connect(txtIP.Text, int.Parse(txtServerPort.Text));
```

3. Change UDP code so that it reads the IP and port address from text boxes.

You will have to read the port values before instantiating the server and client UdpClient objects and then start the 'serverThread' and 'clientThread' threads.

The Client.Send method should send to the IP address entered into a text box.

Remember the port values are integers, whereas the IP address is a string

4. Expand this to the remote chat program, so that one program only needs to be used for can be used

13.14 Summary

In this chapter we have seen the TCP and UDP communications and programs. The TCP program uses separate TCPListener and TCPClient objects and a server which listens on the internet and a client which connects to the server. The code is put into threads and the communication uses Read and Write methods. The UDP application uses UDPClient objects only and connectionless communication using Send and Receive methods.

Both TCP and UDP communication chat programs were developed. The UDP program initially started with a single application that communicated via the internet and 'localhost'. This was extended to two separate applications which communicated on the same PC, and then extended further to communicate across the internet to any internet address.

Chapter 14 - Introduction to Databases

14.1 Introduction

Databases themselves are a vast subject. The following few chapters intend to give you a feel for databases, how to display the data in a database, how to create your own databases and access database data from code.

A database is an integrated collection of data. The most popular database systems are relational databases which consist of separate but linked tables of data. In this way an item of data is held in only one place. Databases are often manipulated and queried using a language called SQL (structured query language). There are also .NET extensions that enable query and other operations, called LINQ (Language-Integrated Query), but we shall not look at these.

In this chapter we will firstly view data in an existing database and secondly create our own database from within the Visual Studio environment. In the next chapter we will see how to display this data on a GUI and then finally access the database using code. To perform these tasks, you must have installed the Visual Studio Database option. If not, you can do so now.

14.2 A typical database

Before we start let's look at a typical database; we shall look at Microsoft's Northwind database. Instructions on downloading this are in the next section. It's a typical relational database that might be used by a company and has separate tables for customers, orders, products, suppliers, etc., all of which are linked together. Figure 14.1 shows a portion of the employees table, which shows the table's rows (the individual employee's data), and columns (or fields): Last Name, First Name etc.

	E	Last Name	First Name	Title	Title C	Birth Date	Hire Date	Address
+	1	Davolio	Nancy	Sales Representative	Ms	08-Dec-1968	01-May-1992	507 - 20th Ave. E.
+	2	Fuller	Andrew	Vice President, Sales	Dr.	19-Feb-1952	14-Aug-1992	908 W. Capital Way
+	3	Leverling	Janet	Sales Representative	Ms	30-Aug-1963	01-Apr-1992	722 Moss Bay Blvd.
+	4	Peacock	Margaret	Sales Representative	Mrs	19-Sep-1958	03-May-1993	4110 Old Redmond Rd
+	5	Buchanan	Steven	Sales Manager	Mr.	04-Mar-1955	17-Oct-1993	14 Garrett Hill
+	6	Suyama	Michael	Sales Representative	Mr.	02-Jul-1963	17-Oct-1993	Coventry House

Employees : Table

Figure 14.1 The Northwind Database

A particular row of a table is called a record and consists of columns, or fields, of data. To link tables, there must be a unique item in each record known as the primary key field; in this case it is the employee's ID. Other columns may have duplicate data though, for example one employee's first name, date of birth or department may be the same as another employee.

Structured Query Language (SQL) provides a set of commands that enable programmers to define complex queries to select the required information from a database. For instance one user might want to know the names of all the employees working in a department but another user, employees over the age of 60, or paid a certain salary. We will look at the basic SQL commands later, but won't get involved in extracting specific data.

14.3 Dealing with Databases

We shall look at the following in this chapter:

1. Inspect and view data in an existing database
2. Creating our own database

In the following chapters we shall see how to use the GUI controls to display data and finally how to access database from code.

14.3.1 Viewing a database in C#

We will start by creating an application that will simply view the Microsoft Northwind database. You may already have this in your PC, but if not you can download it from Microsoft. Instructions for downloading it are at Microsoft's site:

http://msdn.microsoft.com/en-us/library/8b6y4c7s.aspx

Or you can find it by searching for 'Northwind database'.

Download the SQL Server version. The file created is Northwind.sdf (SDF = SQL Server Compact Database File). It seems an unnecessarily complicated process so you might like to refer to the following URL for more information:

http://www.codeproject.com/KB/database/InstallingNorthwindAndPub.aspx

You will also find some excellent projects at this web site.

Alternatively, you can move on to the section 14.4 on creating your own database and then return to this stage.

There are a few differences between the Express and Professional editions of VS2010. In the Express edition the database explorer window is called Database Explorer, but in the Professional edition it is called Solution Explorer.

Start a new windows application and call it 'ViewingADb'. To view and add a database to the project, display either the Database or Server Explorer, depending on the version of Visual Studio you have. To display this window select either View > Server Explorer or View > Other Windows > Database Explorer. This displays a window which has a section called Data Connections.

We will add a connection here to the Northwind database (or other database if you have one). Figure 14.2 shows the Data Connections and the Northwind database tables in the Database Explorer.

Figure 14.2 Database/Server Explorer windows

Add the connection from your program to the database. Right-click 'Data Connections' and choose 'Add Connection'. You can choose from an Access, an SQL Server Compact or a Server Database file. If you downloaded Northwind from the Microsoft site, it is an SQL Server Compact file: select this for the data source and browse for the database. Should you need to, clear the password field. See figure 14.3.

Figure 14.3 Adding a database connection

At this stage you can test that the connection works. Click OK to add the database. It should appear in the Database/Server Explorer window as shown in figure 14.2. If you find you can't access the database, make sure you have access rights, or try copying it to your program folder and try again.

There are different database files: Access database files which have an MDB file extension, SQL Server compact 3.5 database files which have an SDF extension and SQL Server database files which have a MDF file extension. There are others too, such as Oracle database files. The following instructions may vary slightly depending upon which database file you have.

You can now expand the Northwind database in the Explorer. There are a number of Tables and Views. Expand the 'Tables' to see all the individual tables that make up the database.

We can inspect, add or delete the data in the tables by right-clicking the table name in the explorer and selecting 'Show Table Data', see figure 14.4

Figure 14.4 Retrieving database data

If you do this for the Employees table, you will see data similar to figure 14.5. This is of course the same data as we saw in figure 14.1.

Employee ID	Last Name	First Name	Title	Birth Date	Hire Date	Address	City
1	Davolio	Nancy	Sales Represent...	08/12/1948 00:0...	29/03/1991 00:0...	507 - 20th Ave. ...	Seattle
2	Fuller	Andrew	Vice President, ...	19/02/1942 00:0...	12/07/1991 00:0...	908 W. Capital ...	Tacoma
3	Leverling	Janet	Sales Represent...	30/08/1963 00:0...	27/02/1991 00:0...	722 Moss Bay B...	Kirkland
4	Peacock	Margaret	Sales Represent...	19/09/1937 00:0...	30/03/1992 00:0...	4110 Old Redm...	Redmond
5	Buchanan	Steven	Sales Manager	04/03/1955 00:0...	13/09/1992 00:0...	14 Garrett Hill	London
6	Suyama	Michael	Sales Represent...	02/07/1963 00:0...	13/09/1992 00:0...	Coventry Hous...	London
7	King	Robert	Sales Represent...	29/05/1960 00:0...	29/11/1992 00:0...	Edgeham Hollo...	London
8	Callahan	Laura	Inside Sales Co...	09/01/1958 00:0...	30/01/1993 00:0...	4726 - 11th Ave...	Seattle

Figure 14.5 Table Data

You can change the data or add more employees by typing directly into the cells. You must obey the data type and can't type anything into the ID column – this is generated automatically for you. Try this, but you may need to execute the SQL command to update the database. Right-click the cell for the options, see figure 14.6.

Figure 14.6 Execute SQL update

You can delete a row, but note that if you now add more employees, the ID you deleted isn't used again.

Before moving on you might like to look at some of the other tables in this database.

14.4 Creating a new database

As an example of creating a database, let's create our own record collection database. It will have two tables, called Artist and Recording. We will provide a link from the recording to the artist so that on adding a new recording, the user will have to select an artist from the Artist table.

Start a new project and call it CreatingADbase.

To add a new database select Project > Add New Item. You will see you have an option of a Local Database or a Service-based Database, see figure 14.7. Generally a local database (e.g. MS Access) provides a simple data storage and manipulation solution, whereas a service-based database (e.g. SQL server) provides a multi-user solution with the ability to search and manage large amounts of data. Local databases are an SDF file and Service-based database are an MDF file.

Select a Service-based database (MDF file), give it a suitable name (e.g. 'Recordings') and add the database.

Figure 14.7 Adding an SQL database

Cancel the Data Source configuration dialog that appears. We will define the items in the database later. The database connection has been made and appears in the Database/Server Explorer, see figure 14.8.

Figure 14.8 Adding a database

To display Database/Server Explorer, you can double-click the database name in the Solution Explorer or use Views > Other Windows > Database Explorer as you did in section 14.3.1.

As we have seen, if you already have a database you can right-click Data Connections in Database/Server Explorer and browse for the database.

We will now add the tables which make up our database. If you find you don't have all the correct icons, check you have selected and MDF database and not an SDF database.

Let's add our tables. Right-click Tables in the Explorer and select Add New Table. We can now add the names and data types for each column of our database.

Let's create a database for our record collection. We will create tables for artist and recording, but we could also add group/solo artist, date, playing time, genre, record label etc. At a later date we could search for (say) a solo rock and roll artist, dated before 1980 whose playing time is longer than 3 minutes.

The first table we are going to create is for our Artists. It will have a unique ID for the artist.

This database will simply have an ArtistID (an integer variable) and an Artist Name (a number/name variable). Type in ArtistID for the first Column Name with data type 'int' and clear the 'allow Nulls' checkbox. This will be our primary key for this table (the items will be unique). To set this right-click the 'ArtistID' cell and choose 'Set Primary Key' or click the Primary key icon, the one that looks like a key.

It would be useful to automatically generate and increment the ArtistID number as the user adds an artist so, in Column Properties expand the Identity Specification and set (Is Identity) to Yes. The auto-increment value and seed can be changed if necessary.

Add 'Name' for the next Column item and select nvarchar(50) (Variable-length Unicode character data) for the data type and again don't allow nulls.

Your design should be similar to figure 14.9. Save the table (File > Save Table) with a suitable name 'Artist'.

Figure 14.9 Artist database

The table is added to the database. If you get a timeout error, right-click tables in the Explorer and choose 'refresh'. You can now see the table in the Database/Server Explorer.

Add a second table (in Database Explorer, right-click Tables > Add New Table). Add the following column names and data types:

ID, int, no nulls. Add the primary key and identity as before
Title, nvarchar(100) – change the length in the properties, no nulls
PlayingTime, datetime, allow nulls, and
Date, datetime, allow nulls.

We also need to provide a column to link the recording to its artist. This is given the same name as the Artist primary ID.

Add a final column to the Recordings table, with name: ArtistID, data type int and don't allow nulls. The data type must match the Primary Key column we are going to link to i.e. the ArtistID in the Artist table. Your table should be similar to figure 14.10.

Figure 14.10 Recording table

Save the table and call it 'Recording'. We now have two tables defined: 'Artist' and 'Recording'.

14.5 Adding relationships - Database diagrams

We have created two separate tables. We now need add a relationship from the recordings to their artist. To do this we provide a link from the Recording table to the Artist table. This link is known as a foreign key and points to the primary key of the Artist table. In this case is a link from the ArtistID field in the Recording table that matches the primary key ArtistID in the Artist table. When a new recording is added to the database the user will be forced to select an artist for the recording from the Artist table.

We can add a relationship visually using the 'Database Diagrams' in the Database/Server explorer, this link can been seen in figure 14.10.

Right-click Database Diagram and select 'Add a new diagram', click 'yes' to allow the objects to be created and then select and add both the Artist and Recording tables.

The two tables are shown with their fields. To make the link, select the primary key you want to link and drag and drop it to the field in the second table. In this case we want to make a link from the Artists table primary key to the Recording Table so that when we add a recording the user is forced to choose an ArtistID.

Click the ArtistID on the Artist table and drag this to the ArtistID in the Recording table. Note that it makes a relationship name called FK_Recording _Artist, the FK meaning 'foreign key', see figure 14.11. Click OK to close the windows.

Figure 14.11 Linking tables

The database diagram shows the connection between the tables, see figure 14.12. Note the 'one to many' connection. The Artist table has the primary key, and the Recording table the 'infinity' sign, indicating that one unique artist can have unlimited recordings.

Figure 14.12 One to Many database diagram connection

Now let's add some data to our tables. We will add our artists first and then we will be forced to select one when we add our recordings.

Expand the Database/Server Explorer tables to show the Artist and Recording tables. Right-click the Artist table and select 'Show Table Data', see figure 14.13. We can now add our artists.

Figure 14.13 Show Table Data

Click the Name field and add some artists, e.g: Van Morrison, Rolling Stones, Bob Dylan, The Who etc, see figure 14.14. Remember the ArtistID number will be generated for you. This will be used when we link from the recording table.

	ArtistID	Name	
	1	Van Morrison	...
	2	Rolling Stones	...
	3	Bob Dylan	...
	4	The Who	...
▶*	NULL	NULL	

Figure 14.14 Adding Artists to Tables

Now we can add some recordings. Choose 'Show Table Data' for the Recording table and add some titles and artists. You have to use the number you want for the required artist in the ArtistID column, not the artist's name. You will get an error if you try typing in a non-existing number for ArtistID. You will also have to add a complete DateTime data type (8/7/2008 12:59:59, or 1:23:45).

Add the data as shown in figure 14.15, or make up your own titles

ID	Title	PlayingTime	Date	ArtistID
1	Best of Van Morr...	04/09/2007 01:03:00	01/01/1999 00:00:00	1
2	Veedon Fleece	04/09/2007 00:56:00	01/01/1978 00:00:00	1
3	Live at Leeds	04/09/2007 01:03:00	01/01/1972 00:00:00	4
4	Quadrophenia	04/09/2007 01:20:30	01/01/1970 00:00:00	4
5	Sticky Fingers	04/09/2007 00:50:45	01/01/1972 00:00:00	2
NULL	NULL	NULL	NULL	NULL

Figure 14.15 Adding recordings

If you now try to delete 'The Who' from the Artist table you will get an error message, because you have links to it from the Recording table. Data integrity is ensured.

Save the project, we will return to this in the next chapter. The Recordings database is an MDF file (Recordings.mdf) and has been saved in the CreatingaDbase folder.

What we now need to do is display our data in our projects. We'll do that in the next chapter.

14.6 Self Assessment Exercises

1. If you haven't already done so, you can watch the last part (from about 23 minutes in) of the introductory video at:
   http://msdn.microsoft.com/en-us/beginner/bb964631.aspx

2. Watch the tier three video lesson 8 at
   http://msdn.microsoft.com/en-gb/beginner/bb308806.aspx

3. Watch the supporting videos pointed to at Elektor's web site.

4. Open up your Recording database in a new project. Remember it's a Microsoft SQL Server Database (MDF) file (called recordings.mdf) and has been saved in the CreatingADb folder.

5. Create another database this time with three dependent variables. You could extend your record collection to add a third table that holds a library shelf where it is stored.

6. Create a database using names as the primary key. You will of course not need a unique number as an ID, so experiment with the Identity Specification

14.7 Summary

We have discussed databases and looked at a detailed database, Microsoft's Northwind. We have seen how we can include this database in our Visual Studio projects. We have created our own database with two tables (Artist and Recording) from within Visual Studio. Each of these tables has had a primary key and a relationship was established so that when data is added, the user is forced to select an artist for each recording.

We now want our programs to display the data in the database and also write code to access the database to read, write and update the database. In the first case we want a GUI so that a user can see the items in the database and in the second case, code to access the database and add delete or search the database. We'll do that in the next chapters.

Chapter 15 - Displaying databases

15.1 Introduction

So far we have looked at an existing database (Northwind) and also created our own database with linked tables from within Visual Studio. Now we want to design a GUI and write a program to display the database information. We will introduce the GUI database controls, but before we do that, we'll cover some terminology

15.2 The dataset, data binding and ActiveX Data Objects (ADO.NET)

ADO.NET objects create the connection to the database, manage the communication (the requests etc.) between your application and the database, and manage the data that is retrieved as a result of a database query.

The dataset. Database programs do not deal directly with the database when they run; they use a copy known as a dataset and update the database only when required. The dataset can be the whole database or a subset, and holds a collection of data tables related to each other. The DataSet is a class within ADO.NET and we will create a dataset for our program.

Data binding allows data to be retrieved and displayed automatically using the database controls. These controls know how to automatically display and update the various types of data, relieving the programmer of the task.

The binding source is responsible for displaying the current row of data on the form and making sure all the items have the correct and matching data.

We will use a wizard to add all these controls for us. They will appear in the designer tray.

To recap, the Dataset is populated from the database. This is controlled by the TableAdapter which provides the connection and knows how to update the data. The TableAdapterManager controls hierarchical updating of TableAdapters. The BindingSource is responsible for displaying the current row of data on the form and making sure all the items have the correct and matching data, see figure 15.1.

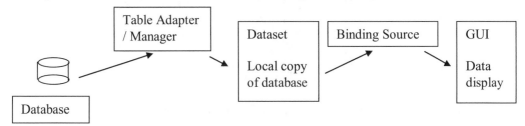

Figure 15.1 Database data transfer

We can choose to display a media-like navigator which enables us to scroll through and update the database data. You can find all these items in the ToolBox and add them yourselves, but there is a wizard that does it all that for you.

15.3 Displaying database information.

Let's return to the Northwind database and display its information in a C# project.

Start a new project and call it DisplayNorthwind. This time we'll use the Data Source Configuration Wizard to add the database. Remember, Access database files have an MDB file extension, SQL Server compact 3.5 database files have an SDF extension and SQL Server database files have a MDF file extension. In this example an SDF database has been used.

Add a new data source (Data > Add New DataSource), select Database > New Connection, and browse for the Northwind database (figure 14.3). Test the connection.

Click 'Yes' to copy the file into your folder, select Tables and finish. See figure 15.2.

Figure 15.2. Adding a data source

We now want to select the data sources to display on our form.

Select Data > Show Data Sources from the main menu to display the dataset, see figure 15.3. If the database isn't displayed, check you have completed the Data Source configuration wizard as above.

Figure 15.3 Customer Data Source

15.3.1 DataGridView

This time, we'll look at the Customers table instead of the Employees table. Click the Customers table (see figure 15.3) and from the drop down box select DataGridView, see figure 15.14.

Figure 15.4 DataGrid view

The DataGridView will display all the data in a grid form. Alternatively, the Details view displays the individual data rows one at a time; we'll see that later.

Drag the Customers' table icon ⊞ (onto the form. This will add a DataGridView and Navigator to the form, see figure 15.5.

Figure 15.5 DataGrid view and Navigator

It will also add the database controls: DataSet, BindingSource, TableAdaptor and TableAdaptorManager to the status bar, see figure 15.6. We will use some of these when we start to access the data from our program.

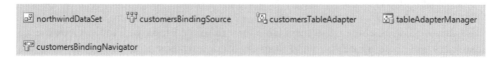

Figure 15.6 Database controls

You can now run the program and see the customer database displayed in a grid format, see figure 15.7.

Figure 15.7 Customer DataGrid display

It's as easy as that! We have done all this without writing a single line of code.

You can now use the Navigator to step through the database and also add new customers and delete them, see figure 15.8.

CustomerID	CompanyName	ContactName	Field1	ContactTitle	Address	City
WANDK	Die Wandernde ...	Rita Müller		Sales Represent...	Adenauerallee 900	Stuttga
WARTH	Wartian Herkku	Pirkko Koskitalo		Accounting Man...	Torikatu 38	Oulu
WELLI	Wellington Import...	Paula Parente		Sales Manager	Rua do Mercado,...	Reserv
WHITC	White Clover Mar...	Karl Jablonski		Owner	305 - 14th Ave. S...	Seattle
WILMK	Wilman Kala	Matti Karttunen		Owner/Marketing...	Keskuskatu 45	Helsink
WOLZA	Wolski Zajazd	Zbyszek Piestrze...		Owner	ul. Filtrowa 68	Warsz
ALWRK	Allwork Co	John		Owner	MMU|	

Figure 15.8 Adding Data

The individual fields are checked for the correct data type when you add a new customer.

You can also save the data but be careful. Depending on your set up, the application may retrieve the original database the next time you run it, and so you will find the data you saved isn't there. This doesn't happen if you run the .EXE file however.

Stop the program and click the tiny box with the right arrow in the top right hand corner of the DataGridView control to display the DataGridView tasks, see figure 15.9. It is here that the data source and editing options can be chosen.

Figure 15.9 DataGridView tasks

You can edit and add columns, and enable adding, editing, deleting and reordering of database entries by your user.

15.3.2 Details view

If you want to see how the Details view works and displays the items repeat the above exercise and select Details instead of the DataGridView, from the drop-down box. You can either do this in a new project, or add the details to the current form.

Figure 15.10 shows the Employees Details selected, note the icon is different from the DataGridView.

Figure 15.10 Details view and icon.

Drag this to the form to show the details view on the form, see figure 15.11.

Figure 15.11 Details display

Each of the controls has its own task that can be selected by clicking the right arrow. For instance you can change the textbox properties to multiline, figure 15.12

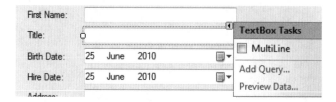

Figure 15.12 Control task options

We will see how to use the Add Query option later.

A navigator should be added to the program. If not you can add a BindingNavigator from the ToolBox Data controls tab. You will have to add the link to the binding source. We'll see this in detail later, but if you want to do it now, select employeesBindingSource from the BindingNavigator 's BindingSource property.

Run the program and note that the employees are displayed one at a time. The correct option appears if you want to alter or add data, for instance, the birth date appears as a DateTimePicker control, see figure 15.13.

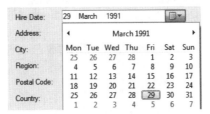

Figure 15.13 DateTimePicker

You can also display individual items from the table on the form. Stop the program and in the Data Sources expand the Employee table. Select PictureBox from the available items. Drag a PictureBox onto the form and click the right-arrow to see the PictureBox tasks, see figure 15.14.

Figure 15.14 PictureBox display

Run the program to see the photographs of the employees, figure 15.15.

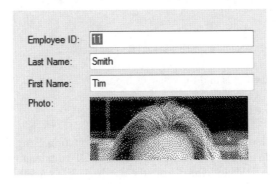

Figure 15.15 Photo Data

15.4 Viewing the data set

The dataset is the memory resident copy of the database. The individual tables of the database and how they are linked can be viewed by clicking the XSD (XML Schema Definition) file displayed in the Solution Explorer, see figure 15.16.

Figure 15.16 Dataset XSD file

The database tables and the links between the tables are displayed, see figure 15.17.

Figure 15.17 The DataSet

You can see the primary fields and the relationships.

15.5 Structured Query Language (SQL)

Finally we will take a look at how we might extract information using Structured Query Language (SQL) commands. If you looked at the SELECT command you would have seen how it defines the fields to extract from the database. It's something like:

SELECT CustomerID, CompanyName, ContactName, Phone FROM Customers

The SELECT command can be qualified in many ways and the basic SQL commands are shown in Table 15.1. We won't need to use any of these commands, letting the wizard generate them instead, but you might find it useful to know some of the commands to see how the data is extracted from the database.

SQL keyword	Description
SELECT	Selects fields from one or more tables
FROM	Specifies the table(s) from which to retrieve the data. - Required for SELECT and DELETE commands
WHERE	Specifies criteria that determines the rows to be retrieved
GROUP BY	Specifies criteria for grouping records
ORDER BY	Specifies criteria for ordering records
INSERT	Inserts data into a table
UPDATE	Updates data in a table
DELETE	Deletes data from a table

Table 15.1 SQL commands

We shall briefly discuss these commands.

The SELECT command.

The SELECT query is used to select or get information from a table. The basic form is:

SELECT fields FROM tableName

All the fields from the Northwind employee's table were selected using:

SELECT * FROM employees

We can select specific fields by replacing the asterisk with the field name. For example:

SELECT firstName, lastName FROM employees

The WHERE command.

In most cases users want to look for specific data with the fields. The WHERE command is used to specify the selection. The simplest format of the WHERE command is:

SELECT field FROM tableName WHERE criteria

For example to select all the users called John from the database you might use:

SELECT firstName, lastName FROM employees WHERE firstName = John

The WHERE condition can contain the usual operators ($<$,$>$, $<=$, $>=$, $==$, $<>$) as well as LIKE. LIKE can be used with a wildcard. For example, to get first names beginning with J, as follows:

SELECT firstName, lastName FROM employee WHERE firstName LIKE 'J*'

The INSERT command

The INSERT command inserts a new record in a table. The simplest form for this is:

INSERT INTO tableName (fieldname(s)) VALUES (value(s))

For example:

INSERT INTO employees(firstName, lastName) VALUES ('Joe', 'ALLWORK')

The UPDATE command

Changes are made only to a local copy of the database. The UPDATE command is used to save these changes. The simplest form is:

UPDATE tableName SET fieldname = value WHERE criteria

For example:

UPDATE employees SET lastName = 'ALLWORK'
WHERE lastName = DOE and firstName = 'Jane'

This will change the last name of the record for Jane DOE to ALLWORK.

The DELETE command

The DELETE command will delete data from a table. The simplest form is:

DELETE FROM tableName WHERE criteria

For example we could delete the record for Jane ALLWORK using the command:

DELETE FROM employees WHERE firstName = 'Jane' AND lastName =
'ALLWORK'

15.6 Query Builder

Now that we now slightly more about SQL, we can briefly return to the 'Add Query, we saw in section15.12. If you clicked on this you saw an SQL criteria builder dialog appear, figure 15.18.

Figure 15.18 SQL Criteria Builder

Clicking on Query Builder, displays the dialog shown in figure 15.19.

Figure 15.19 Query Builder

Here you can select and deselect the fields you want included in the query, order them by dragging their details, add a filter (LIKE 'Tim') and the query is built for you. By clicking Execute Query, you can see the result. In this example, an employee's first name has been changed, so that two Tim's are displayed.

15.7 Self Assessment Exercises and errors

SQLServer error

If your database isn't working, make sure the SQLServer is running.
Try: All Programs > Microsoft SQLServer > Configuration tools > SQL Server Configuration Manager
  Select SQL Server services, and check that the SQL Server is running, see figure 15.20.

Figure 15.20 SQL Server Configuration Manager

Exercises

1. Watch the tier three video lesson 9 at
    a. http://msdn.microsoft.com/en-gb/beginner/bb308806.aspx

2. Watch the supporting videos pointed to at Elektor's web site.

3. Create your own database from within Visual Studio.

4. Display the Artist and Recording tables from last chapter's database using both DataGridView and Details views.

5. Add a selection of individual items for the same item to the form, for example: for the recording date display a DateTimePicker, a TextBox, a Label etc.

Remember, depending on how you coped your database, you may only be able to keep your saved data if you run the .EXE file, not if you re-compile from within Visual Studio.

15.8 Summary

In this chapter we have seen how data is extracted from the database with a table adaptor, creating a local memory resident copy of the database (the dataset), the items of which are displayed using controls which are binding sources, i.e. 'bound' to the data, and change automatically as the user interacts with them.

The DataSource configuration wizard was used to select the DataGridView to display all the table's fields in a grid form and the database information was displayed. The individual database items were also displayed using the Details view. We have seen the DataGrid view tasks such as adding, editing and deleting. A navigator was automatically placed on the form and as the user scrolls through the database the views automatically change; they are bound to the data.

The SQL language which is used to access the data in the database has briefly been covered. In our case the wizard created the SQL statement we needed, but the SQL query builder was also seen.

In the next chapter we will see how to extract the data from the database and deal with this in our code, for example to save data collected from a database.

Chapter 16 - Accessing a database with code

16.1 Introduction.

We have seen how to display the contents of a database, create our own database and display the data in a GUI using DataGrid and Details views. We will now see how to access the data in a database from code and either extract or add data to the database.

We shall create our own general data logger database and write code to read that, but there is an example using Northwind on the Microsoft website at: http://msdn.microsoft.com/en-us/library/0f92s97z.aspx.

16.2 Creating the database

We will create a simple single table database and write code to navigate and update the database. We will add our own navigation buttons rather than use the Navigator tool or grid view tasks, so that you understand the process in adding, deleting and updating a database.

We will create the database from within Visual Studio, but if you prefer you can create it in Access. If you do this, remember to check the database type created. If you are unsure about any of the steps, refer back to chapter 14.

16.2.1 Creating a database from within Visual Studio

Start a new project and add a service-based Project > Add New Item > Service-based Database and call it Logger, see figure 16.1.

Figure 16.1 Adding a database

Note that the database is an MDF file. Remember an Access database is an MDB file and we saw earlier the SQL Server compact 3.5 database SDF file type.

We will add the dataset file to our application later, so cancel the rest of the Data Source Configuration Wizard, see figure 16.2.

Figure 16.2 Data Source Configuration Wizard

The (empty) database will appear in the Server/Database explorer. Display the explorer, expand the Logger database and right-click Tables to add a new table, see figure 16.3.

Figure 16.3 Adding a New Table

Add the data types as shown in figure 16.4. Don't allow any nulls

Column Name	Data Type	Allow Nulls
ID	int	☐
Setpoint	int	☐
Temperature	float	☐
Time	smalldatetime	☐

Figure 16.4 Table data types

Set the ID field's Identity Specification 'Is Identity' to 'Yes'. Make it a primary key.

Save the table (File > Save) and call it LoggerTable. It will be added it to the Tables in the Logger database.

We can now add data to our database. Expand the Tables, right-click LoggerTable and select Show Table Data, see figure 16.5. This will enable you to add data.

Figure 16.5 Show table data

Add some data. Remember you don't have to enter data into the ID field. Ignore the exclamation marks which are just a reminder that the data hasn't been saved.

	ID	Setpoint	Temperature	Time
	1	18	23.4	27/05/2010 17:12:00
	2	19	22.2	27/05/2010 17:13:00
	3	14	18.7	27/05/2010 17:14:00
🖉	NULL	21	❶ NULL	NULL
✳	NULL	NULL	NULL	NULL

Figure 16.6 Adding data

Save and close the project. The database will be in the program's folder.

16.3 Displaying the database.

Now that we have a database, let's display the items before moving on to change the database. This is covered in the previous chapter, but we shall repeat it briefly here.

Start a new project. Add the Data Source connection: in Server/Database Explorer, right-click DataConnections and choose Add connection. This time select the SQL Server Database (MDF file) unless you created an Access Database (MDB) file, and browse for it. If necessary clear the User name box. Test the connection and click OK, see figure 16.7.

Figure 16.7 Adding the data source connection

16.3.1 Add the Data Source

To add the data source to the project, choose Data > Add New Data Source to display the Data Source Configuration Wizard. Select 'Database' and the data source, and Dataset as the Database model. Click Next. The data connection that has just been created should be selected but if not, select New Connection and repeat the process. Click Next to add the database.

At this stage you may get a message asking if you would like to copy the database to your folders. If you say yes to this, a copy of the database will be made each time the program runs which means that any changes you make will be overwritten the next time you run the program.

16.3.2 Select Database Objects

The wizard now requests your database objects, see figure 16.8. Select Tables and click Finish. You could have selected just a field from a table, if that is all you want to display.

Figure 16.8 Adding Database objects.

We now have a database called Logger with a table called LoggerTable, a connection called loggerConnectionString, a table adaptor called LoggerTableTableAdapter and a dataset (memory resident version of the database) called loggerDataSet. To refresh your memory on how these all link together, see figure 15.1. To see the individual database fields, expand the database in database explorer, see figure 16.9. To see the fields we can add to the form, expand the database in the data sources window, see figure 16.10.

Figure 16.9 Database fields

Before we add individual Details view controls, check your database access works by displaying the items in a DataGridView as we did before. Display the DataSources (Data > Show Data Sources), select the Logger table and ensure DataGridView is selected. Click and drag the Logger table to the form, see figure 16.10.

Figure 16.10 Data Sources Window

Check the DataGridView tasks (click arrow in top right-hand corner) and check the editing options as shown in figure 16.11.

Figure 16.11 DataGridView tasks

Run the program. Because we allowed editing, you can now add data to your database by typing in the fields, see figure 16.12.

ID	Setpoint	Temperature	Time
1	18	23.4	27/05/2010 17:12
2	19	22.2	27/05/2010 17:13
3	14	18.7	27/05/2010 17:14
4	21	20.9	27/05/2010 17:15
5	25	23.3	27/05/2010 18:16
6	26	26.6	27/05/2010 18:17

Figure 16.12 Database display

Although '-1' is displayed for the ID whilst entering new data, on saving the correct ID is recorded.

Remember that, depending on your setting, on restarting the program the original database may be obtained not the updated one.

16.3.3 Accessing the database from code

To see how we can display the database items from our code we'll add our own navigation controls, even though the navigator toolbar is available. We shall read the database values and display them using a MessageBox and add new values to the database from textboxes.

Start by adding controls so we can add data to the database. Add two labels and two textboxes to allow the user to add a new set point and temperature (call them txtSP and txtTemp).

Add buttons First, Next and Add (btnFirst, btnNext and btnAdd) so that your design is similar to figure 16.13.

Figure 16.13 Program GUI

Declare a pointer to the current database row and a DataRow type:

```
public int rowPosition = 0;
public DataRow drAdd ;          // see later
```

The DataRow class represents a row of data in a table, and later we will fill all the DataRow's fields with data before adding the row.

The cells in the database are accessed by the row position and the column name or index, like a two dimensional array. So the ID of the a row is accessed using:

```
loggerTable.Rows[rowPosition]["ID"]
```

and the first row's ID would be:

```
loggerTable.Rows[0]["ID"]
```

Add the following method to display the rows. We shall call this from the First and Next button clicks.

```
private void ShowCurrentRecord()
{
  if (this.loggerDataSet.loggerTable.Rows.Count != 0)
  {
    MessageBox.Show("ID="+
```

```
this.loggerDataSet.loggerTable.Rows[rowPosition]["ID"].ToString()+
      ", Setpoint=" +
this.loggerDataSet.loggerTable.Rows[rowPosition]["Setpoint"].ToString() +
      ", Temperature=" +
this.loggerDataSet.loggerTable.Rows[rowPosition]["Temperature"].ToString() +
      ", Time=" +
this.loggerDataSet.loggerTable.Rows[rowPosition]["Time"].ToString());
      }
   }
```

If you get errors when you enter this code, it's most probably upper/lower case errors, so check the names and the case of identifiers. Let the IntelliSense prompt you.

Add the following code for the First, Next and Add buttons:

```
private void btnFirst_Click(object sender, EventArgs e)
    {
        rowPosition = 0;
        ShowCurrentRecord();
    }

private void btnNext_Click(object sender, EventArgs e)
    {
        if (rowPosition<this.loggerDataSet.loggerTable.Rows.Count-1)
        {
            rowPosition++;
        }
        ShowCurrentRecord();
    }
```

I'll let you work out how you might add 'Previous' and 'Last' buttons.

Now let's add code to add data. We use the DataRow we declared at the top and add the contents for each field. I have also added the current time.

```
private void btnAdd_Click(object sender, EventArgs e)
{
    // check we have something to add
    if ((txtSP.Text != String.Empty) || (txtTemp.Text != String.Empty))
    {
        drAdd = this.loggerDataSet.loggerTable.NewRow();
        drAdd["ID"] = this.loggerDataSet.loggerTable.Rows.Count+1;
        drAdd["Setpoint"] = int.Parse(txtSP.Text);
        drAdd["Temperature"] = float.Parse(txtTemp.Text);
        DateTime theTime = new DateTime();
        theTime = DateTime.Now;
```

```
                drAdd["Time"] = theTime.ToShortTimeString();
                this.loggerDataSet.loggerTable.Rows.Add(drAdd);
            }
        }
```

The program should now run and you can add data to the database from your code, see figure 16.14.

ID	Setpoint	Temperature	Time
1	18	23.4	27/05/2010 17:12
2	19	22.2	27/05/2010 17:13
3	14	18.7	27/05/2010 17:14
4	21	20.9	27/05/2010 17:15
5	12	12.19999980926...	27/06/2010 20:34
6	13	13	27/06/2010 20:35

16.3 Displaying a database

First   Next   Add

Setpoint 13   Temperature 13

Figure 16.4 Adding data GUI

16.3.4 Update the Database

At the moment only the memory resident dataset is updated. To update the database on the disk, add an Update button and the following code:

```
private void btnUpdate_Click(object sender, EventArgs e)
{
    try
    {
    // validate control
    this.Validate();
    // end the editing to allow update
    this.loggerTableBindingSource.EndEdit();
    // Update all the changes in the dataset
    this.tableAdapterManager.UpdateAll(this.loggerDataSet);
    }
```

```
        catch (SystemException ex)
        {
            MessageBox.Show("Update failed" + ex.ToString());
        }
    }
```

Note the TableAdapterManager is responsible for updating the database. This was a new component in VS2008 and organizes the TableAdapters in updating hierarchical databases.

Remember that depending on how you created or copied the database, the original may not be updated. On re-running the application the original database may be retrieved. You can see this if you search for your database. You will see the original database and the copy (which is the one your program updates). For more information on this, refer to the Microsoft web site at: http://msdn.microsoft.com/en-us/library/ms233817.aspx

16.4 Reading and saving nulls in database

You may read or write a null from/to a database, rather than using a default value. The item to check for is DBNull.Value.

Reading Null values from a database

Null values read from a database can be converted to a string without a problem, e.g.:

```
txtTemp.Text = this.DataSet.Table.Rows[rowPosition]["temp"].ToString();
```

However, if you want to use a value such as an integer, you have to check that it's not a null entry on the database before using it. For example the following code will check for a null in the database and use the (integer) value if not:

```
if (this.DataSet.Table.Rows[rowPosition]["sp"] != DBNull.Value)
{
    int tempSP = (int)this.DataSet1.Table.Rows[rowPosition]["sp"];
}
```

Of course, if you want to use a default value instead of a null you can do so, just add an else clause. (else tempSP = -1;)

Saving Null values in a database

In this example a floating point value is read from a textbox. If the textbox is empty, dbNull.Value is saved in the database; otherwise the textbox's value is used:

```
if (txtTemp.Text == String.Empty)
        drAdd["temp"] = DBNull.Value;
```

```
        else
                drAdd["temp"] = float.Parse(txtTemp.Text);
```

16.5 Self Assessment Exercises

1. Watch the 'Using an Access Database' video at:
   http://msdn.microsoft.com/en-gb/beginner/dd571507.aspx

2. Watch the supporting videos pointed to at Elektor's web site.

3. Add buttons in the program for Last and Previous commands.

4. Write a program that automatically generates a set point, a temperature and a time, say on a Timer event, and adds these values to the database.

5. Create your own database and add values to it.

16.6 Summary

In this chapter we have seen how to create a database from within Visual Studio and to add this data source to a program. Initially the data was displayed using a DataGridView and navigator controls as we did in the last chapter, but this time we have added our own navigation controls and read the database using the database table property with row and column, and written to the database using DataRow data type.

Now we know how to access data in a database, we will now see how to plot the data or, in fact, plot any data points.

Chapter 17 - Plotting and Charts

17.1 Introduction

As we have seen, .NET does not have any plotting controls or classes. In this chapter we will see how to use a third party add-on called NPlot. This is available from the NPlot Wiki site: www.netcontrols.org. Documentation is available at: netcontrols.org/nplot/downloads/nplot_introduction.pdf.

17.2 Plotting with Nplot

Nplot provides a selection of charts, including line plot, point plot, step plot, candle plot, bar plot and image plot. They are shown in figure 17.1

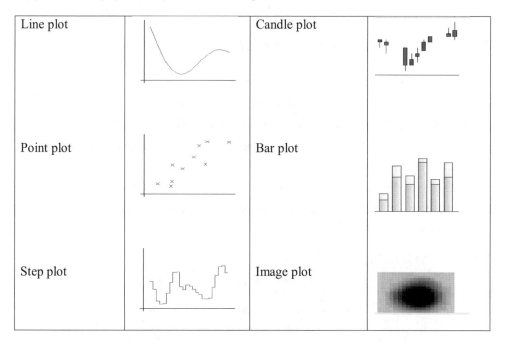

Figure 17.1 Types of plot

We shall see how to define the type of plot, data, axes, scales etc. in this chapter.

17.3 Obtaining the software.

To obtain the software, download and extract the zipped file from the web site at:
        http://netcontrols.org/nplot/wiki/index.php?n=Main.DownloadArea

If you have problems, check that your firewall isn't hindering the installation.

17.4 Adding NPlot to your project

Having downloaded and extracted the file, you need to add the Nplot classes to your project. The process is summarised here, but you can also follow the Windows Forms Tutorial (C#) on the NPlot wiki web site, see figure 17.2.

Figure 17.2 Nplot Wiki web site

1. Open Visual Studio and create or open your project.
2. Open the toolbox and right click on any item. Select Choose Items ...
3. Select the .NET Framework Components tab, click Browse.
4. Find the extracted NPlot folder and open the bin > net > 2.0 > release folder and select NPlot.dll. Click open.
5. Make sure the PlotSurface2D control is checked and click OK, see figure 17.3.
6. The PlotSurface2D control appears in the toolbox, and you can now use it like any other toolbox control.

Figure 17.3 .NET components

If you have problems installing NPlot, check that your firewall is not stopping you. If you have problems running Nplot, refer to the wiki, where there are several help pages.

You also need to make sure your project includes a reference to the NPlot library.

Open the solutions explorer and expand References. Make sure Nplot is referenced, see figure 17.4. If not, right click the References header and select Add Reference. Click Browse and locate the NPlot dll file (NPlot folder>bin>net>2.0>release). Click OK.

Figure 17.4 NPlot reference

You also need to do one more task with VS2010 and .Net Framework 4. You need to retarget your application to run for .NET Framework 4, rather than the default .NET Framework 4 Client Profile. I don't know what the difference is either, but you will have to right-click 'Properties' in the Solution Explorer, click Open and change the Target Framework to .NET 4, see Figure 17.5.

Figure 17.5 Retarget .NET Framework

17.5 NPlot Windows Form Tutorial

Having done all that, you can follow the rest of the NPlot tutorial on the NPlot wiki web site. Figure 17.6 shows the graphs generated.

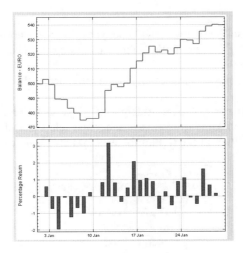

Figure 17.6 NPlot Windows Tutorial display.

As suggested, for a more dynamic display, set the DateTimeToolTip property for each control to true. The DateTimeToolTip changes the date display as the cursor is moved over the graph.

17.6 Drawing a graph

Let's find out more about the coding and how to draw a graph. If you're like me, you most probably haven't thought about the process of drawing a graph since you were at school. You have to work out what the range of values are for the axes, what scales you are going to use and their labels, the grid (horizontal and vertical), the size and colour of the pen and the data values themselves. All of these need to be defined in your code when drawing the graph.

The axes that are available are shown in figure 17.7:

Figure 17.7 NPlot axes

The axes' scales are automatically determined, but you might want to add a label, tick text, and the angle of the text.

At this stage we should also mentioned how the data is specified. The following can be used:

1. A DataSet, DataTable or DataView. (Useful for databases)
2. A collection:
      a. Double[ ]
      b. System.Collections.ArrayList
      c. System.Collections.Generic.List<Int16>

We will use a List collection to hold our X and Y data values.

17.7 Graph exercise.

Let's try plotting the graph of sine(x)/x. This is quite a pretty graph. It has a maximum Y value of +1, when X=0. We shall plot it over ±50 radians.

To see different graph types, we'll start with a step plot and then change it to a line plot.

Start a new project. Add using NPlot; at the top of the code. Check that Nplot is shown in the references.

Add a plotSurface2D control on the form. Change its name to plotSurfaceSineX. We'll draw the grid first. Add the following code after InitializeComponent( );

```
// clear the surface
plotSurfaceSineX.Clear();

//Add a background grid.
Grid grid = new Grid();
grid.VerticalGridType = Grid.GridType.Coarse;
grid.HorizontalGridType = Grid.GridType.Coarse;
grid.MajorGridPen = new Pen(Color.LightGray, 1.0f);

plotSurfaceSineX.Add(grid);
```

You can of course be lead by the IntelliSense and see the other options available.

Follow the code you have typed with code for a step-plot graph – we shall see how to get a smooth curve later.

```
//Create a step plot instance for the sineX chart.
StepPlot stpSineX = new StepPlot();
// choose Pen colour and size
stpSineX.Pen = new Pen(Color.Blue, 2);
```

Now add the lists to which the points will be added and from which be drawn. There are two, one for the X-axis and one for the Y-axis (SineX/X).

```
//Create the lists from which to get the data.
List<float> XAxis = new List<float>();
List<float> sineXoverX = new List<float>();
```

Now let's add the X values and calculate the Y:

```
//Add data to X axis lists.
float range = 50.0F;
float f = -range;
while (f<=range)     // start at -50.0
{
    XAxis.Add(f);      // add the X value
    f=f+0.5F;
    // and calculate Yvalues – check we don't divide by zero
    if (f == 0)
    {
        sineXoverX.Add(1);
    }
    else
    {
        sineXoverX.Add((float)Math.Sin(f) / f);
    }
}
```

Now we set up the data source and X axis for the plot and add to the plot. Note that this uses the step plot object, stpSineX that we declared above.

```
//Set the x-axis (abscissa) and datasource for the plot.
stpSineX.AbscissaData = XAxis;
stpSineX.DataSource = sineXoverX;
```

```
//Add the stpSineX to plot.
plotSurfaceSineX.Add(stpSineX);
```

Set up the general plot settings:

```
// Plot general settings.
plotSurfaceSineX.ShowCoordinates = true;
```

```
plotSurfaceSineX.YAxis1.Label = "SineX over X";
plotSurfaceSineX.YAxis1.LabelOffsetAbsolute = true;
plotSurfaceSineX.YAxis1.LabelOffset = 40;
plotSurfaceSineX.XAxis1.HideTickText = false; // true;
plotSurfaceSineX.Padding = 5;
```

And finally refresh the surface to draw it;

```
//Refresh surface.
plotSurfaceSineX.Refresh();
```

All this code has been added in the public Form1( ) { code.

If you now run the program, you should get a plot like figure 17.8:

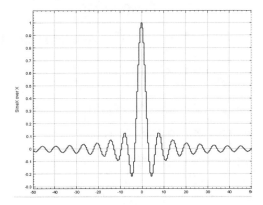

Figure 17.8 SineX/X step plot

If it doesn't work, remember to add Nplot to the References, add 'using Nplot;' at the top of the code, and retarget your application to .NET Framework 4.

17.7.1 Different graph types.

Let's try some different plot types. Try a point plot, replace the code

```
StepPlot stpSineX = new StepPlot( );
```
with:
```
PointPlot stpSineX = new PointPlot( );
```

As a PointPlot doesn't use a Pen, comment out the line:

```
stpSineX.Pen = new Pen(Color.Black, 2);
```

This displays a point plot as shown in figure 17.9.

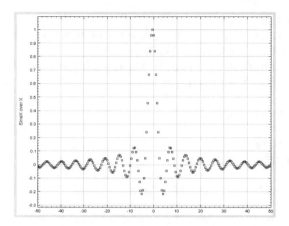

Figure 17.9 Point plot

Or for a smooth graph, see figure 17.10, replace the same lines with a Line Plot:

```
LinePlot stpSineX = new LinePlot();
```

And re-instate the Pen:

```
stpSineX.Pen = new Pen(Color.Blue, 2);
```

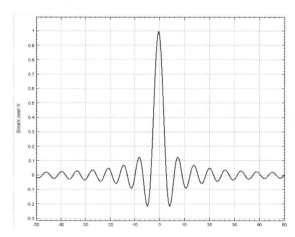

Figure 17.10 Point plot

17.8 Self Assessment Exercises

1. Now that you know the basic process for plotting a graph, try adding a legend for the X axis.
Hint:

```
stpSineX.Label = "Step Label";  // for legend
Legend stepLegend = new Legend();
```

```
stepLegend.AttachTo(PlotSurface2D.XAxisPosition.Bottom,
        PlotSurface2D.YAxisPosition.Right);
plotSurface2D1.Legend = stepLegend;
```

2. Draw individual graphs of:

        a) $y = \log(x)$;
        b) $y = x-5$;

3. Try to draw the graphs on the same graph and see if there is a solution to the equation:

$$x-5 = \log(x);$$

4. Try different data sources for your graph such as a double[] array, or a database dataset.

5. Investigate another 3rd party charting package, called Zedgraph.

17.9 Summary

We have introduced a third party plot control from NPlot. We have seen the types of plots this can draw. We downloaded and added the control to the toolbox and followed the NPlot tutorial to seen it running. We have seen the steps involved in drawing the graph, and written our own program to plot a graph on a form.

Chapter 18 - Dynamic link libraries (DLL) and using Windows API

18.1 Introduction

You will soon have written some useful methods which you may want to use in other programs. Of course you could cut and paste the code into each new program, but there is a better way. By saving your code as a dynamic link library (DLL) and providing a link to it from your new program you can just call and use it. The code will be loaded by the program when needed. Be careful however, if at that time it's not available you will get a run-time error so you must include it with your executable.

18.2 Writing a DLL

Let's try this with a simple example. We will create our own namespace, which we will add to our code with a using statement. This will have a class that contains the methods we will use in our program.

Let's take the method we used in the chapter on Methods, which to take an integer and return its square root. The method is:

```
double SquareRoot ( int intRoot)
{
  return Math.Sqrt(intRoot);
}
```

We create our DLL by starting a new project, but this time choosing Class Library instead of a Windows Forms Application, see figure 18.1. Give it a sensible name. I've used MyMathLibrary.

Windows Forms Application	Visual C#
WPF Application	Visual C#
Console Application	Visual C#
Class Library	Visual C#
WPF Browser Application	Visual C#
Empty Project	Visual C#

Figure18.1 Creating a DLL

The following code with Class1 is created. We will add our own class and delete Class1.

```
namespace MyMathLibrary
{
    public class Class1
    {
    }
}
```

Figure 18.1a

Add a new Class (Project>Add Class) and give it the name MyMathClass, see figure 18.2

Figure 18.2 Adding a new DLL class

VS2010 will remove the empty Class1 but, if you need to, you can remove Class1.cs by selecting it in the solution explorer and pressing the delete key.

Add the SquareRoot method to our class as shown below and save the project. The class must be declared public. We could add further mathematics classes in MyMathLibrary. You might want to save all your DLLs in their own folder.

```
namespace MyMathLibrary
{
    public class MyMathClass
    {
        public double SquareRoot(int intRoot)
        {
            return Math.Sqrt(intRoot);
        }
    }
}
```

Build your DLL solution (press the F6 key) and save the project. Note that if you try to run the program, you will get an error message that says the Class Library cannot be started directly.

18.3 Calling the DLL

Start a new Windows application (I've called it myMathDLLDemo). This program will call our DLL code.

We'll make it really simple and display the square root in a message box when a button is clicked.

You have to let your program know about your DLL. Add the using statement at the top of the code:

using MyMathLibrary;

Add the DLL to the References. Use Project > Add reference, click the Browse tab, and browse for MyMathDLL.dll (it's in MyMathLibrary > bin > release). You can now see it in References in the solution explorer, see figure 18.3

Figure 18.3 MyMathLibrary DLL reference

Add a button to a form and for the button click, change the code to the following:

```
private void button1_Click(object sender, EventArgs e)
{
    MyMathClass myMathObj = new MyMathClass();
    MessageBox.Show((myMathObj.SquareRoot(5)).ToString());
}
```

Note that the IntelliSense knows about MyMathClass and the SquareRoot method and prompts as you type; see figure 18.4. If the SquareRoot method isn't displayed, check that both the class and the method were originally declared as public.

Figure 18.4 The IntelliSense display

Run the program to check it works. Your display should be similar to figure 18.5.

Figure 18.5 Program UI and output

18.4 Static Classes

In this case we had to instantiate the **myMathObj** object before we could use it. We don't have to do this for the normal Math methods, so how can we do this for ours? If you remember, declaring a method as 'static' let's us do this. We'll see how to do this now.

Return to the MyMathLibrary and add the Square method as follows:

```
static public double Square(double dblSquare)
{
    return dblSquare * dblSquare;
}
```

Build the project and save it.

Return to myMathDLLDemo and change the code to the following:

```
private void button1_Click(object sender, EventArgs e)
{
    // declare math object
    MyMathClass myMathObj = new MyMathClass();
    // use Square root method
    double mySqRt5 = myMathObj.SquareRoot(5);
    // square it - no need to instantiate
    double fiveSquared = MyMathLibrary.MyMathClass.Square(mySqRt5);
    // and display
    MessageBox.Show(fiveSquared.ToString());
}
```

We still have to instantiate the **myMathObj** object from the MyMathClass, but we can now use the Square method without instantiating any objects. We have used this directly with the code:

    MyMathLibrary.MyMathClass.Square(mySqRt5);

You don't have to include the **MyMathLibrary** if you don't want to.

Note that as you type, the IntelliSense knows about the Square method but not the SquareRoot, see figure 18.6.

```
// square it - no need to instantiate
double fiveSquared = MyMathLibrary.MyMathClass.|
// and display
MessageBox.Show(fiveSquared.ToString());
```

| Equals |
| ReferenceEquals |
| Square |

Figure 18.6 Square method

18.5 Windows Application Program Interface (API)

This is a good point to introduce the Windows Application Programming Interface and the DLL calls provided that enable access to the Windows operating system and Windows services such as file handling, mouse and keyboard interfacing. Of course many of these can be made through the .NET libraries, but .NET programs run slower than truly compiled programs such as C++ and programs that use API calls run faster.

The API calls are held in three main namespaces:

- Base services – file systems, threads, error handling (kernel32.dll)
- Graphics devices interface – output to output devices and to draw windows and dialog boxes (gdi32.dll)
- User interface – manages windows and controls, mouse and keyboard inputs (user32.dll)

It is easy to use the API calls once you know what calls are available and they are described at the Platform Invoke web site at www.pinvoke.net, which also has examples.

Pinvoke.net also a Visual Studio add-in that enables programmers to access the calls directly.

18.6 Using Win API calls

The API calls are held in an external library, so you must add the namespace:

    using System.Runtime.InteropServices;

Declare the API call. For example to add the call to make your computer beep, add the declaration:

```
[DllImport("User32.dll")]
static extern Boolean MessageBeep(UInt32 beepType);
```

(Note that's DLLImport, not DLLLmport or DIlImport)

In this case the MessageBeep is held in the User32.DLL library, it's a static member and is implemented externally (extern). It is passed a UInt32 data type, and returns nothing.

To call the MessageBeep API, use the code (say on a button click):

```
MessageBeep(0);
```

A more versatile API called Beep is also available. This plays a frequency for a specific duration. The declaration is:

```
[DllImport("kernel32.dll", SetLastError=true)]
[return: MarshalAs(UnmanagedType.Bool)]
static extern bool Beep(uint dwFreq, uint dwDuration);
```

Let's not get into marshaled code and unmanaged data types!

Example code to play a 1 kHz tone for ½ second (500 ms) is:

```
Beep (1000, 500);
```

We will return to this when we look at using DirectX for audio output.

18.7 MessageBox API example

As an example, let's call the MessageBox API. This is similar to the MessageBox.Show call we are familiar with.

Start a new project and add the following using clause at the top of the code:

```
using System.Runtime.InteropServices;
```

Before 'public Form1()', add the DLL declaration code that displays the MessageBox:

```
[DllImport("User32.dll")]
public static extern int MessageBox(int h, string m, string c, int type);
```

Add a button to a form and add the following code:

MessageBox(0, "API Message", "API title", 0);

Figure 18.7 MessageBox API call

Run the program to check it works and displays the message box shown in figure 18.7.

You can see how the message and title are passed to the MessageBox display. The final parameter controls the icon and the buttons displayed, for instance the value 1 displays OK and Cancel buttons and 2 displays 'Abort, Retry, Ignore'.

This API call also returns a value, depending on which button was pressed. This can be checked with the following code:

```
int returnValue = MessageBox(0, "API Message", "API title", 2);
System.Windows.Forms.MessageBox.Show(returnValue.ToString());
```

Notice how we have had to put the full definition of the Windows MessageBox call to determine the difference between that and the API call.

More information on this and all the other calls can be found on the pinvoke.net web site.

18.8 Playing sounds

We can play a tone using the Beep call, but we can play wav files using the PlaySound API. The DLL declaration is:

```
[DllImport("winmm.dll")]
public static extern long PlaySound
        (string lpszName, long hModule, long dwFlags);
```

To play the sound simply use the code:

```
PlaySound("C:\\WINDOWS\\Media\\tada.wav", 0, 1);
```

The MessageBox API is found in the User32.dll library and the PlaySound is in the winmm.dll library, so how do we find out in which DLL group our call is? If you type the call into pinvoke's search, you should find it. For instance the results for the MessageBeep search are shown in figure 18.8, and that it's in the user32 library.

Figure 18.8 Pinvoke search result

A DLL can optionally define an entry point. We will see this in the hardware interfacing chapter where we use the input / output DLL (inpout.dll) which has two entry points: one for input and one for output.

18.9 Unsafe code

Unsafe code allows us direct access to memory and generally involves the use of pointers. You should not use unsafe code if you can help it, but sometimes it is unavoidable. For instance:

- When real time applications need to enhance performance
- For external functions and some Windows APIs
- In debugging, when we need to access memory

As an example of using unsafe code, we shall look at the GetComputerName API call. This uses a pointer to pass both a buffer and the buffer's size. To allow your project to compile and run unsafe code, label the code as unsafe and tell VS2010.

In a new project, add using System.Runtime.InteropServices; and add the DLL declaration, before the code public Form1( ):

```
[DllImport("Kernel32.dll")]
static extern unsafe bool GetComputerName(byte* lpBuffer, long* nSize);
```

Add a button on the form, and change its click code to:

```
private void button1_Click(object sender, EventArgs e)
{
    byte[] byteArray = new byte[512];
    long size = byteArray.Length;
    unsafe
    {
```

```
        long* pSize = &size;
        fixed (byte* pBuffor = byteArray)
        {
            GetComputerName(pBuffor, pSize);
        }
    }
    System.Text.Encoding textEnc =
            new System.Text.ASCIIEncoding();
    MessageBox.Show("Computer name: " +
            textEnc.GetString(byteArray));
}
```

We've not seen the asterisk and the ampersand before (e.g. long* pSize = &size;). It's C code for a pointer into (or the address of) memory, in this case holding a pointer to a long variable called pSize.

You have to state the size of the data being pointed to (e.g. long*). Pointers can be incremented, and so one pointing to a byte variable would only be incremented by one byte, whereas one pointing to a Uint32 would have to be incremented by four bytes.

To compile the unsafe code, open the project's Properties page. (Project > programName > Properties), click the Build property page and select the 'Allow Unsafe Code' check box, see figure 18.9

Figure 18.9 Compiling unsafe code

Compile and run the program – it should display your computer's name, see figure 18.10.

Figure 18.10 GetComputerName display

Incidentally, there is a 'safe' version of this, and should really be used. The declaration is:

[System.Runtime.InteropServices.DllImport("Kernel32", CharSet=CharSet.Auto)]
public static extern bool GetComputerName(StringBuilder buffer, ref uint size);

The code is now:

```
byte[] byteArray = new byte[512];
StringBuilder strBuilder = new StringBuilder();
uint usize = (uint)byteArray.Length;

GetComputerName(strBuilder, ref usize);
MessageBox.Show("Computer name: " + strBuilder.ToString());
```

18.10 DLL for measuring time

There are two ways we know of measuring time: the timer component and the Ticks property of the DateTime structure. The resolution of these is stated as 1 ms and 100ns respectively. But due to overheads you never get this resolution; it's more like 16ms.

If your system supports a high-resolution counter, it is possible to get a better resolution using the QueryPerformanceCounter and QueryPerformanceFrequency DLLs. These provide a much more accurate measurement of time. These calls are defined in the Kernel32 library. Detailed information is found at:
http://support.microsoft.com/default.aspx?scid=KB;en-us;Q172338

Even this reference suggests the resolution for these are 10ms.

To use these components you need to know what clock frequency is being used to clock the counter, and then you can read the counter and hence calculate the time between counter values. The following exercise will display the clock frequency and the minimum resolution (the time taken to read the counter).

Start a new project and add using System.Runtime.InteropServices; at the top of your code. Add the following DLL declarations:

```
[DllImport("kernel32.dll")]
extern static short QueryPerformanceCounter(ref long x);

[DllImport("kernel32.dll")]
extern static short QueryPerformanceFrequency(ref long x);
```

The long data types are passed by ref.

For a button click event code add the following:

```
long count1 = 0, count2 = 0, freq = 0;
```

```
// if the Performance counter returns a value other than zero, there must be one
    if (QueryPerformanceCounter(ref count1) != 0)        // Begin timing.
    {
        QueryPerformanceFrequency(ref freq);             // find frequency
        QueryPerformanceCounter(ref count1);             // read counter
        QueryPerformanceCounter(ref count2);             // and read again

        MessageBox.Show("Start Value: " + count1 +
            ". End Value: " + count2 + "\r\n" +
            "Clock frequency is: " + freq + "\r\n" +
            "Resolution: 1/freq = " + (int)1000000000 / freq +
            " nanoseconds." + "\r\n" + "Time to read counter: " +
            (count2 - count1) * 1.0 / freq + " seconds.");
    }
    else
        MessageBox.Show("High-resolution counter not supported.");
```

Figure 18.11 shows the output for a couple of my computers. The first shows a clock frequency of 3.5MHz, giving a resolution of 279 nanoseconds, but actually takes 1.95 microseconds to read the performance counter, so this is the best timing I can get.

Figure 18.11 Performance frequency and counter

18.11 Self Assessment Exercises:

DLL
1. Add some extra Math classes. It doesn't matter if they are already defined in the Math namespace. Try adding DLLs that need to be instantiated and some that don't i.e. that are declared as static.

API
2. Look at some of the API calls at the pinvoke web site. Search for the Beep API. Note that it can be overridden to include a frequency and duration:

    ```
    static extern bool Beep(uint dwFreq, uint dwDuration);
    ```

3. Write a program to play a beep of your own frequency and duration. Combine this to play a short tune.

Timing
4. Write a program to read find out the resolution of your PC using ticks and DateTime.Now. Compare this with the resolution obtained with the performance APIs

18.12 Summary

We have seen how we can create a Windows Library class and add methods, saving them as Dynamic Link and Locate (DLL) code. We have seen how we add the DLL reference and call the DLL code from other projects. We have also seen that by declaring a method as static, we don't have to instantiate an object to use the method.

We have covered Windows API calls and seen how they allow us direct access to the operating system using some simple examples. We have discussed using unsafe code. Finally we have seen how we can use the Performance frequency and Performance counter to obtain better timings from our PC.

Chapter 19 - Hardware interfacing

19.1 Introduction

In this chapter we will look at the traditional serial and parallel ports and see how we can interface to them using the serial IO control in Visual Studio and through DLL calls. In the next chapters we will study analogue interfacing using the sound card inputs and outputs, and USB interfacing firstly using a commercial product and finally to our own USB PIC design.

19.2 The Serial and Parallel ports.

The serial and parallel ports have served designers well over the life of the PC, and although are being replaced by USB are still a need to use these to interface to a PC, not least of all connecting to legacy hardware.

There is plenty of information on these ports, so apart from the pin connections described later, no further detail will be provided. We will however get some idea of how to interface to these ports from our C# programs.

19.3 Visual Studio Serial Port control

Visual Studio has a control that performs serial input and output. It is the SerialPort control and found in the Components toolbox tab, see figure 19.1.

 SerialPort

Figure 19.1 The Serial Port control

It is a non visual control. Its main properties are set to a common communications rate and are: BaudRate: 9600, DataBits: 8, Parity: None, PortName: COM1, StopBits: One.

Its main event is: DataReceived which occurs when data is received from the port.

19.4 Serial Port example program

The SerialPort control can easily be demonstrated with a connector plugged into the serial port that has transmit and receive pins (2 and 3) connected together. We will design a program that reads from a textbox and sends this data to the serial port; it then displays the data received via the serial port on a list box.

Start a new program and call it SerialPortIO. Don't call it serialIO, as this may get confused with the namespace with that name.

This program will read data typed into a text box and send it to the serial port and display the data received by the serial port in a list box.

Place a list box, a textbox and a SerialPort control from the components toolbox on the form; use the default names, see figure 19.2.

Figure 19.2 Serial port design

Make sure the SerialPort's properties are set to the defaults above. You may have to change COM1: to another COM port if it's already being used.

The SerialPort class is in the System.IO.Ports namespace, so add the 'using' statement at the top of the code:

```
using System.IO.Ports;
```

Change the form load event to the following. Of course we can set these values at design time, but it shows how to change the values at run-time. The Parity and StopBits are defined in System.IO.Ports.

```
private void Form1_Load(object sender, EventArgs e)
{
    serialPort1.BaudRate = 9600;
    serialPort1.DataBits = 8;
    serialPort1.Parity = Parity.None;
    serialPort1.StopBits = StopBits.One;
    serialPort1.Open();
}
```

We will use the serial port's WriteLine and ReadLine methods to send and read the data. Find the text box's key down event and change its code to the following:

```
private void textBox1_KeyDown(object sender, KeyEventArgs e)
{
```

```
    if (e.KeyCode == Keys.Enter)
    {
        serialPort1.WriteLine(textBox1.Text);
        listBox1.Items.Add(serialPort1.ReadLine());
        textBox1.Clear();
    }
}
```

Run the program. When the Enter key is pressed the data in the textbox is sent to the serial port using the WriteLine method. The echoed data is read by the ReadLine method and the data is displayed in the list box.

Ideally this program should really be written using threads, with one thread for the WriteLine and one for the ReadLine.

Alternatively the SerialPort's DataReceived event can be used. This runs as a thread and so to write directly to the listbox in the form load event, add the code:

```
    CheckForIllegalCrossThreadCalls = false;
```

Add the following to the SerialPort's dataReceived event, and remove the listBox.Items.Add code from the keydown event.

```
    private void serialPort1_DataReceived(object sender,
    SerialDataReceivedEventArgs e)
    {
        listBox1.Items.Add(serialPort1.ReadLine() );
    }
```

The program should run and echo the data as before.

This program also works with USB to serial adaptors, but you have to change the serial port PortName from COM1 to something like COM17.

19.5 Serial Port connections

For completeness, I have included the serial port connections. A PC may have a 25-way or 9-way 'D' type connector. Both pin-outs are shown in Table 19.1.

Signal Name	9-way connection	25-way connection
n/c	1	1
RxD	2	3
TxD	3	2
DTR /	4	20
0V GND	5	7

DSR /	6	6
RTS /	7	4
CTS /	8	5
n/c	9	

Table 19.1 Serial port connections

Note that if you want to connect two computers together, you have to cross-over the Tx and Rx data lines, i.e. connect pin 2 on one PC to pin 3 on the other, and vice versa. You can generally manage with using just pins 2, 3 and a ground.

19.6 The parallel printer interface.

There have been a few designs of parallel interface during the life of the PC and so it is difficult to know which your user may have. The original was controlled by the following registers:

Data register: Bits 0-7 data
Status Register: Bits: 0-2 not used, 3-Error, 4-Select, 5-paper out, 6-acknowledge, 7 busy.
Control Register: Bits: 0 strobe, 1-Auto-feed, 2-initialise, 3-select, 4-IRQ enable, 5-7 N/A

The LPT1 parallel port base address (data register) is at 0x378, with status and control at 0x379 and 0x37A respectively.

To send data to a printer the data is written to the data register and the strobe line is pulsed. However instead of driving a printer, the port can be used to control input and output lines. But whilst there are eight outputs only those from the status register are guaranteed inputs.

19.7 Printer port connections

The printer port connections are shown in Table 19.2

PC -25 way D socket	Signal	Direction	Centronics Printer 36 way
1	Strobe/	→	1
2	Data 0	→	2
3	Data 1	→	3
4	Data 2	→	4
5	Data 3	→	5
6	Data 4	→	6
7	Data 5	→	7
8	Data 6	→	8
9	Data 7	→	9
10	Acknowledge/	←	10

11	Busy	←	11
12	Paper out	←	12
13	Select	←	13
14	Auto Feed	→	14
15	Error/	→	15
16	Initialise/	→	16
17	Select input/	→	17
18 -25	GND		19 -36

Table 19.2 Printer port lines

19.8 Accessing the parallel port

The parallel port can be accessed using the inpout32.dll which is available via Jan Axelson's Lake View Research useful web site (www.lvr.com). The DLL provides direct read and write of the I/O ports and so could be used to drive the serial port. The file and more information on the dll is available at http://logix4u.net/Legacy_Ports/Parallel_Port.html

Note that there is now a 64-bit version of this.

You have to put the inpout32.dll file into your debug or release folder.

Let's design a program that will light some LEDs attached to the parallel port.

19.8.1 The hardware

To display the output of the parallel port, just attach some LEDs to it. They should be connected from pins 2 to 9 to ground (pins 18 - 25). LEDs with integral resistors are now available which makes it simple. If you don't use them, you will have to include resistor of about 470Ω for each LED.

19.8.2 The software

Our design will have eight buttons, the colour of which (Red or Gray) will reflect the state of the LEDs attached to the parallel port.

Start a new project and place 8 buttons on the form. For each of these set the BackColor to Web > Gray. I have given each of the buttons text: bit0, bit1 etc. Bit0 is on the right, see figure 19.3.

When we click a button we will change the state of the LED and the colour of the button to match the LED.

Figure 19.3 Parallel port GUI

Start a new project. Add 'using System.Runtime.InteropServices;' at the top of the code so that we can use DLLImport.

After the code: public partial class Form1 : Form {, add the following class code so that we can call the DLL:

```
public class PortIO
{
  [DllImport("inpout32.dll", EntryPoint = "Out32")]
  public static extern void Output(int adress, int value);
}
```

If you haven't done so, place the inpout32.dll in the debug or release folder. You don't have to add this to the references.

Declare the variables:

```
int ledState = 0;                    // record of the output state
const int BASEADDRESS = 0x378;       // Parallel port base address
```

Now add the reset code in the form load event:

```
// reset port and remember state of LEDs
ledState = 0;
PortIO.Output(BASEADDRESS, ledState);
button1.BackColor = Color.Gray;
button2.BackColor = Color.Gray;
button3.BackColor = Color.Gray;
button4.BackColor = Color.Gray;
button5.BackColor = Color.Gray;
button6.BackColor = Color.Gray;
button7.BackColor = Color.Gray;
button8.BackColor = Color.Gray;
```

and for each button click add the set/reset code:

```
//Button1 (bit 0) Button Click code
```

```
if (button1.BackColor == Color.Red)
{
    button1.BackColor = Color.Gray;
    ledState = ledState & 0xFE;    // turn bit 0 off
}
else
{
    button1.BackColor = Color.Red;
    ledState = ledState | 0x01;    // turn bit 0 on
}
PortIO.Output(BASEADDRESS, ledState);

//Button 2 (bit 1) Button Click code
if (button2.BackColor == Color.Red)
{
    button2.BackColor = Color.Gray;
    ledState = ledState & 0xFD;    // turn bit 1 off
}
else
{
    button2.BackColor = Color.Red;
    ledState = ledState | 0x02;    // turn bit 1 on
}
PortIO.Output(BASEADDRESS, ledState);
```

// and the same for Button3 (bit2) etc.

Note the AND and the OR logic commands turn the individual bits on and off without affecting the other bits. Add the code for the rest of the buttons. The other off/on values are:

Bit	OFF	ON
2	0xFB	0x04
3	0xF7	0x08
4	0xEF	0x10
5	0xDF	0x20
6	0xBF	0x40
7	0x7F	0x80

This code looks very inefficient to me and I'm sure there's a really neat way of doing it, for instnce by using an array of buttons, but it works.

Plug in your LED display and run the program. You should be able to switch the LEDs on and off from the program.

19.8.3 Parallel port inputs

The inpout32.dll can also be used to input signals via the parallel port. In this case the dll is declared with Inp32 as its entry point, as:

```
[DllImport("inpout32.dll", EntryPoint = "Inp32")]
public static extern int Input(int address);
```

With the parallel port address declared as:

```
const int PARPORT = 0x378;
```

then the Control register is read using the code

```
int temp = Input(PARPORT + 2);
```

The individual bits of temp can be determined by ANDing and ORing with the required values as we did in the previous example.

19.9 Self Assessment Exercises.

1. Connect to PCs with a null-modem serial cable (one with pins 2 and 3 crossed over) and write a chat program so that users on two separate PCs can communicate.

2. Extend this program so that files can be transferred between the PCs.

3. Connect some parallel outputs to inputs and write a program to set the outputs and read the inputs. Remember only some parallel port bits are guaranteed to be inputs.

4. Connect some switches to the parallel port and write a program to read the state of the switches. You will have to check which lines are capable of input.

19.10 Summary

In this chapter we have covered interfacing with the serial and parallel ports. The former using the SerialPort toolbox control and the latter using an external DLL. A simple parallel output design driving LEDs was studied. In the next chapter we shall look at using the sound card as analogue input and output, and after that interfacing to the PC using the USB port.

Chapter 20 - Using the sound card and DirectX drivers

20.1 Introduction

In this chapter, we will see how we can provide analogue input and output from the PC by using the Microsoft DirectX drivers that interface to the sound card.

We will start by introducing the DirectX drivers and then see how these are used to generate an analogue output via the headphone / loudspeaker socket.

We will then see how the DirectX drivers are used to read the microphone or line-in input and develop a simple oscilloscope application using the nPlot graph seen in Chapter 17.

20.2 DirectX

Microsoft's DirectX is a collection of APIs used for games programming and multimedia (the X stands for the individual applications, e.g. DirectSound). It provides a common interface so that code for each individual sound or graphics card doesn't have to be written. In this chapter we will use the DirectInput API for input and the DirectSound API for output.

The software development kit (SDK) is available from Microsoft DirectX Developer Center and the first version to support VS2010 was in June 2010. It's 571Mb and needs 1.2 GB disk space. Needless to say it takes some time to install and if you already have the DirectX drivers, is most probably unnecessary for what we want to do. This version only supports VS2010 and C++, but we will see how we can use DirectX with VS2010 and C#.

Before we start coding, let's take a look at the DirectX classes we will need.

20.3 The DirectX components

20.3.1 The DirectSound class.

This provides the interface between your programs the sound card drivers. It provides some advanced techniques such as mixing and adding effects. DirectSound3D also exists which provides a 3D surround sound effect. These two are now referred to as DirectX Audio. XAudio 2 is a cross-platform (Windows and Xbox) API, intended as the replacement for DirectSound. To play sounds, the DirectSound class needs a DirectSound device object which provides the basic interface and drivers for the sound device (sound card).

20.3.2 The DirectInput class

This class collects input from input devices such as the mouse and keyboard. In our case we will be using the microphone or line-in as our input device. We will see how we can determine which input devices are available.

20.3.3 Cooperative level

The Cooperative level determines how much control of the hardware your program is allowed. The available levels are:

- Normal – The primary buffer (see later) is set to 22 kHz, stereo, 8-bit and it can't be written to.
- Priority – The primary buffer format can be set by the application. This should be used as it gives the most robust behaviour whilst allowing the user some control.
- Write-Primary – The application has direct access to the primary buffer

In the following examples when we play a WAV file, we'll use the Normal cooperative level. If we don't want to be restricted by sampling rate, nor need direct access to the primary buffer, we will use the Priority cooperative level. This provides control over the sound format and allows other programs that use sounds to play.

20.3.4 The Buffers

The Primary and Secondary Buffers

The buffers hold the sounds being played. The primary buffer is the one that the sound card plays. The secondary buffer (SecondaryBuffer class) provides a higher level interface to the device. There may be more than one secondary buffer; these have the effects applied to them and sounds mixed before being transferred to the primary buffer. We will use secondary buffers.

Short sound samples can be loaded completely into the secondary buffer and played, but as audio can take up a lot of memory a few second's worth of data is normally transferred into the secondary buffer and streamed. Your program then fills the buffer as the sound plays. Events can be set to occur when the buffer is nearly empty (or full in the case of capturing data), but we won't use those here.

The Capture Buffer

When it comes to capturing the sound inputs, the opposite happens. A capture buffer (CaptureBuffer class) is filled and your program empties it. The CaptureBuffer has methods such as Start, Stop, Read and Write.

The capture buffer captures the signal from a Capture object (the input device), and saves it into an array of bytes with the specified wave format (WaveFormat).

Like the SecondaryBuffer, this can either stop capturing when the buffer is full or can be a streaming buffer which your program has to empty before the data is overwritten. The easiest way is for your program to find out the current position of the write buffer pointer and empty the buffer at the correct point. Alternatively a Notify event can be set up which fires at the right time.

20.3.5 The input device

Your PC may have many inputs and outputs that can be used. Your program needs to know which one it is using. It also needs to know the wave format, i.e. the sampling rate, number of channels and number of bits per sample. Later we will see how to set up the correct formats and choose an input device.

20.4 Playing sounds

Before using the DirectX libraries, remember that we saw in chapter 18 how to play sounds using the API calls 'Beep' and 'PlaySound'. These are much simpler to use than the examples we will see here and may be good enough for your needs.

There are five steps involved in using DirectX to play sounds:

1. Create the output device to be used to play the sound,
2. Set the cooperative level,
3. Create the buffers and their description,
4. Fill the buffer(s),
5. Play the sound (and repeat 4 if necessary until done)

In this first example we will play a WAV file.

Start a new project and save it. Right click the project's name in Solution Explorer, select Properties and change the target .NET framework to version 3.5, see figure 20.1. This has to be done, because the latest versions of DirectX only support C++.

Figure 20.1 Re-targeting the .NET framework

Add the Microsoft.DirectX.DirectSound driver DLL to the program's References, see figure 20.2. You will have to browse for them. My drivers were in the folder: Windows/Microsoft.NET/DirectX for Managed Code/1.0.2902.0.

Figure 20.2 Adding DirectX references

Add the using statement: using Microsoft.DirectX.DirectSound;

Before public Form1(), add the declarations for the output device and secondary buffer:

```
private Device outputDevice;
private SecondaryBuffer sbufSound;
```

The following code instantiates an output device, the cooperative level and the SecondaryBuffer and description. It also loads the sound file to be played.

Add the following sound initialization code after InitializeComponent();

```
// instantiate a new Device
outputDevice = new Device();
// Set the Cooperative level – to normal, we don't want to do anything
clever
outputDevice.SetCooperativeLevel(this, CooperativeLevel.Normal);
// instantiate a new Bufferdescription
BufferDescription bfrDesc = new BufferDescription();
// load the sound into the secondary buffer
sbufSound = new SecondaryBuffer
        (@"C:\windows\media\tada.wav", bfrDesc, outputDevice);
```

The BufferDescription contains the properties and methods of the secondary buffer we create. Ensure the tada.wav exists in the folder, or find another suitable wav file.

Add a button and the following code for its click event:

sbufSound.Play(0, BufferPlayFlags.Default);

Compile the code. If you get the error 'LoaderLock was detected", go to Debug > Exceptions > Managed Debugging Assistants and uncheck LoaderLock, see figure 20.3.

Figure 20.3 LoaderLock exception

Clicking the button should play your sound.

20.5 Playing waveforms

In this example we will generate and play a buffer that contains the data for a sine wave. The values for the sine wave will be calculated and put into the secondary buffer in place of tada.wav using the secondaryBuffer.Write() method.

This time we will need to know what the properties are of wave format we are using. For example: the sampling rate, the number of bits per sample, the number of channels and the coding used for the waveform.

This is the DirectSound WaveFormat structure. The properties are:

AverageBytesPerSecond	The average data-transfer rate in bytes per second. For example, 16-bit stereo at 44.1 kHz has an average data rate of (2 bytes per sample * 2 channels * 44,100 samples per second) is 176,400 bytes per second.
BitsPerSample	The number of bits per sample.
BlockAlign	The minimum atomic unit of data in bytes. The product of Channels and BitsPerSample divided by 8.
Channels	The number of channels used.

FormatTag	The waveform-audio format type. (PCM = raw data)
SamplesPerSecond	The sample rate, in samples per second (hertz).

The user interface is the same as the previous example. The complete code is:

```
using System;
using System.Windows.Forms;
using Microsoft.DirectX.DirectSound;

namespace CreatingSounds
{
    public partial class Form1 : Form
    {
        private Device outputDevice;
        public Form1()
        {
            InitializeComponent();
            // instantiate a new Device
            outputDevice = new Device();
            // Can also use Cooperative level – Normal
            // SetCooperativeLevel args are owner and level
            outputDevice.SetCooperativeLevel(this, CooperativeLevel.Priority);
        }
        private void button1_Click(object sender, EventArgs e)
        {
            int sampleRate = 44100;
            int duration = 2;              // seconds
            const double FREQ = 554;       // C# ! (A(4)=440)

            WaveFormat format = new WaveFormat();
            // set up WaveFormat properties
            format.BitsPerSample = 8;
            format.Channels = 1;
            format.BlockAlign = 1;              // Channels * BitsPerSample / 8.
            format.FormatTag = WaveFormatTag.Pcm;
            format.SamplesPerSecond = sampleRate;
            format.AverageBytesPerSecond =
                    format.SamplesPerSecond * format.BlockAlign;

            // Now set up buffers
            BufferDescription bfrDesc = new BufferDescription(format);
            bfrDesc.DeferLocation = true;     // can assign at playing time
            bfrDesc.BufferBytes = 8 * format.AverageBytesPerSecond;

            // calculate data
```

```
byte[] sineData = new byte[sampleRate * duration];
for (int i = 0; i < sampleRate * duration; i++)
{
    sineData[i] = (byte)(128 + (127 * Math.Sin
        (2*Math.PI* i * FREQ / sampleRate)));
}

// set up secondary buffer
SecondaryBuffer sbfrSound =
        new SecondaryBuffer(bfrDesc, outputDevice);

// load the sound into the buffer = lock buffer whilst doing it
sbfrSound.Write(0, sineData, LockFlag.EntireBuffer);
// and play it (perhaps there should be a delay here, but it works)
sbfrSound.Play(0, BufferPlayFlags.Default);
        }
    }
}
```

Obviously your program could have some selection boxes for the desired frequency, duration, sample rate, etc.

More information on the DirectSound classes and methods can be found on the Microsoft library at: http://msdn.microsoft.com/en-us/library/bb318665(VS.85).aspx

20.6 Detecting input devices

Before we start to perform any capturing, we need to find out which input devices are available. These are held in a CaptureDevicesCollection – a collection of DeviceInformation structures that contains the properties for each input device. The devices are easily found in a couple of lines of code.

In a new project perform the usual steps to set up the correct environment.

At the top of the code add the statement: 'using Microsoft.DirectX.DirectSound;'.

We'll let the program find the devices when the form loads and display them in a comboBox. Add a comboBox to the form and call it 'cmbCaptureDevices'. Add the following code for the form load event:

```
private void Form1_Load(object sender, EventArgs e)
{
    CaptureDevicesCollection myDevices = new
CaptureDevicesCollection();

    // Display in combobox
```

```
        foreach (DeviceInformation Devinfo in myDevices)
            cmbCaptureDevices.Items.Add(Devinfo.Description);
    }
```

Your output should be similar to figure 20.4:

Figure 20.4 Capture devices

Now the name of your device is known, your program could select a suitable input or the input device could be seleted from the comboBox by the user.

20.7 Capturing sounds

We can now try using the sound card's input channels to capture the input waveforms. The procedure is similar to the playing sounds, but instead of defining the format, filling an array and transferring this to the buffer to be played, the format is defined, a capture buffer set up and the data captured. The data is then in an array that can be read and played if desired. We shall display the data on a graph.

The procedure is as follows:

1. Set up the capture format: the sample rate, the number of bits per sample, the number of channels and the wave format.
2. Calculate the block alignment for the buffer and the average bytes per second.
3. Calculate the capture buffer size and if using events, set up the notify size.
4. Determine the capture device input and create a Capture object and CaptureBuffer for the required input device and format determined in 1).
5. If echoing the data, create the output device, format and buffers as we did in the previous section. Two buffers may be required – one to play from whilst the other is loaded from the capture buffer. This should really using threads.
6. Start capturing and read the capture buffer pointer position. Empty the buffer when required. Alternatively, create and run a thread that reads the capture buffer into an array when notified event occurs. Play the sound if required.

We have seen 1), 2), 4) and 5). We have also discussed the role of the capture buffer. This is filled until either the required capture position is read, or if using threads, the notify size is met.

We will now look at capturing an input and displaying the waveform using nPlot.

20.8 Capturing sound program

In a new project add an Nplot Surface that will display the waveform, two buttons to start and stop the recording (btnStart and btnStop – set their Enable propertry to false) and a combobox to select the input device (cmbDevices).

The Start button will be enabled when the user has selected an input device from the combobox. The Start button will start the capturing and disable itself. The Stop button will be enabled once the data has been captured. Pressing the Stop button will display the waveform and re-enable the Start button.

The design should be similar to figure 20.5

Figure 20.5 Sound capture user interface

Now set up the right environment:
- re-target .NET framework to version 3.5,
- Disable check for loader lock,
- Add Nplot to references,
- Add the Microsoft.DirectX.DirectSound driver DLL to the program's References

Add the using statements:

```
using Microsoft.DirectX.DirectSound;
using NPlot;
```

before Form1 () add the declarations:

```
public System.Array read;
public int captureBfrSize;
```

```
public CaptureBuffer captureBfr;
public int capturePos, readPos = 0;

CaptureDevicesCollection myDevices = new CaptureDevicesCollection();
```

In the form() initialization code add:

```
CheckForIllegalCrossThreadCalls = false;
```

Change the Form Load event to:

```
private void Form1_Load(object sender, EventArgs e)
{
    // Display in combobox
    foreach (DeviceInformation Devinfo in myDevices)
        cmbDevices.Items.Add(Devinfo.Description);
}
```

Change the comboBox SelectedIndexChanged event to enable the Start button:

```
private void cmbDevices_SelectedIndexChanged(object sender, EventArgs e)
{
    btnStart.Enabled = true;
}
```

For the Stop button the code is:

```
private void btnStop_Click(object sender, EventArgs e)
{
    // reset buttons, display sound – the last SMALLAMPSIZE (256) bytes
    // from readPos

    const int SMALLAMPSIZE = 256;
    btnStop.Enabled = false;
    btnStart.Enabled = true;
    // plot it
    plotSurface2D1.Clear();
    Grid grid = new Grid();
    grid.VerticalGridType = Grid.GridType.Coarse;
    grid.HorizontalGridType = Grid.GridType.Coarse;
    grid.MajorGridPen = new Pen(Color.LightGray, 1.0f);
    plotSurface2D1.Add(grid);
    LinePlot pltSound = new LinePlot();
    pltSound.Pen = new Pen(Color.Blue, 2);
    List<float> XAxis = new List<float>();
    for (int i = 0; i < SMALLAMPSIZE; i++)
```

```
    {
        XAxis.Add(i);
    }
    Double[] Amplitude = new Double[48000];
            // 96000 for one channel, or equal to sample rate
    Double[] smallAmp = new Double[SMALLAMPSIZE];

    read.CopyTo(Amplitude, 0);

    int startPos = readPos - SMALLAMPSIZE - 256;

    // display most recent SMALLAMPSIZE items
    for (int i = startPos; i < startPos + SMALLAMPSIZE; i++)
    {
        smallAmp[i - startPos] = Amplitude[i];
        // smallAmp[i] = Amplitude[i];
    }
    pltSound.AbscissaData = XAxis;
    pltSound.DataSource = smallAmp;
    plotSurface2D1.Add(pltSound);
    plotSurface2D1.Refresh();   // plot!
}
```

Finally add the code to capture the sound, when the Start button is clicked:

```
private void btnStart_Click(object sender, EventArgs e)
{
    btnStart.Enabled = false;

    var format = new WaveFormat
    {
        SamplesPerSecond = 48000,   // or 96000 etc
        BitsPerSample = 8,              // or 16
        Channels = 1,                   // or 2 for stereo
        FormatTag = WaveFormatTag.Pcm   // raw data
    };

    // Calculate BlockAlign and AverageBytesPerSecond
    format.BlockAlign = (short)(format.Channels *
            (format.BitsPerSample / 8));
    format.AverageBytesPerSecond =
            format.SamplesPerSecond * format.BlockAlign;

    captureBfrSize = (format.SamplesPerSecond *
            format.BitsPerSample / 8) * 2;
    // 2 seconds - but we'll stop after 1
```

```
// Create Capture buffer and CaptureBufferDescriptor
var cap = default(Capture);

// find device selected in comboBox and create Capture object
for (int i = 0; i < myDevices.Count; i++)
{
    if (myDevices[i].Description.ToLower().
        Contains(cmbDevices.SelectedItem.ToString().ToLower()))
    {
        cap = new Capture(myDevices[i].DriverGuid);
        break;
    }
}

var capDesc = new CaptureBufferDescription
{
    Format = format,
    BufferBytes = captureBfrSize
};

captureBfr = new CaptureBuffer(capDesc, cap);

// Start capturing

captureBfr.Start(true);

/************
 * loop waiting for capture buffer to be filled
 * use GetCurrentPosition.
 * see http://msdn.microsoft.com/en-us/library/bb280835.aspx
 * *************/

captureBfr.GetCurrentPosition(out capturePos, out readPos);

// Not sure how often we can read capturePos, so stop after 1 second
while (capturePos < captureBfrSize / 2)
    captureBfr.GetCurrentPosition(out capturePos, out readPos);

// stop capturing
captureBfr.Stop();

// and copy the buffer
read = captureBfr.Read(0, typeof(byte), LockFlag.None,
        captureBfrSize / 2);

// free resources
```

```
        captureBfr.Dispose();
        cap.Dispose();
        btnStop.Enabled = true;    // enable stop button
}
```

Run the code. Figure 20.6 shows what I get when I whistle into my microphone.

Figure 20.6 Sound capture display

20.9 Self Assessment exercises

1. Try different sampling rates and plot these.

2. The sampling rate should be at least twice the highest freqency of the signal. Observe what happens when the sampling rate is near (or less than) that rate.

3. Change the sample code so that the display is permanently updated.

4. Change the sample code so that the graph displays time along the x-axis.

5. Find out how to use threads and events to control Direct Input.

6. Look at the example of capturing and playing sounds at the same time at: http://khason.net/blog/capturing-and-streaming-sound-by-using-directsound-with-c

7. Study the DirectX Audio examples in the SDK.

8. For further hardware designs, you can read the book: 'Complete Practical Measurement Systems using a PC' by Yury Magda, published by Elektor.

20.10 Summary

This has been a whirlwind introduction to the DirectX libraries and only touched on a couple of them. The basics of using the DirectX classes (buffers, etc.) and setting up the I/O devices have been covered. The DirectSound library has been used to play a .WAV file and also play a software generated waveform. Finally the DirectInput library has been used to detect the input devices and record and display a sound input.

We have also seen the problems of running DirectX and C# under VS2010 and seen how to work-around this.

Chapter 21 - USB interfacing

21.1 Introduction

The USB port is now the most popular way of interfacing peripherals to the PC. A complete USB design involves designing the USB product hardware as well as software for the product itself and drivers for the PC, and this will be covered in the next two chapters. However, it may be that you don't want to go into that detail, can't manufacture any hardware, or just want to make it easy by buying in some hardware. We will consider the latter in the chapter.

If you want a simple USB interface, integrated circuits are available which provide a direct USB to serial and USB to parallel interface, for example the FT232R and FT245R devices from Future Technology Devices International (FTDI). If you want a simple non-programmable interface these are worth considering. Of course many manufacturers make USB products you can program with your code (e.g. Cypress, Velleman and Microchip PIC products).

DLP Design Inc. (www.dlpdesign.com) manufactures a USB/Microcontroller module which uses the FT245R device as its USB interface and also contains a PIC. The module is the DLP-245PB-G and we shall study a design using this device. This not only provides the USB interface and all the drivers we need for both the PC and USB ends, but also contains a programmed Microchip PIC microcontroller which responds to basic I/O commands. This can also be programmed for your needs.

21.2 The USB interface

We do not need to know much about the USB interface to get the module design working, so we shall not cover the USB interface in detail here. Suffice it to say, the USB consortium (www.usb.org) governs the protocol and standards of USB. Whilst anyone can make a USB product, it cannot display the 'USB Certified' logo without the consortium evaluating it. They will provide you with a unique vendor ID (VID). You can either register your own VID for approximately $2000 or you can use FTDI's for free with the module. For more information, refer to: http://www.dlpdesign.com/usb-prev/vid.shtml.

USB version 2.0 specifies three modes of operation: High speed (480 Mbits/s), Full speed (12 Mbits/s) and Low speed (1.5 Mbits/s). The USB interface uses four wires, two for power and two data lines called D+ and D-. The USB device itself indicates its presence and speed by pulling either the D+ or D- data line high. A super-speed USB specification has now been released.

Your device can take its power from the USB bus but if so, stringent rules must be met.

The host (i.e. your PC) controls the USB bus and initiates and controls all messages to the slaves. There can be up to 127 devices on the bus and hence a device may not run at its maximum speed. USB On-The-Go has now been specified to allow slaves to communicate with each other (e.g. a digital camera to a printer). For more information on any of these refer to the usb.org web site.

The USB connectors come in a few limited types. The standard A-type is exclusively for a host (e.g. your PC) and the B-types are for connection to slaves. These can be seen in figure 21.1. Smaller Micro A and B-types connectors are available for small devices such as PDAs, phones and cameras.

Figure 21.1 DLP-245PB-G module.

21.3 USB Module installation and hardware

We will create a USB design using the DLP Design's DLP-245PB-G module. DLP Design is based in Allen, Texas and FTDI are one of their distributors in the UK. Figure 21.1 shows the device with an LED and switch attached for our program example.

The module features:

- USB 1.0 and 2.0 compatible – communication at up to 2Mbits/s
- 18 digital I/O lines (6 as A/D inputs)
- Programmable Microchip 16F877A PIC
- Pre-programmed code to interface to USB providing access to the I/O, EEPROM and external digital temperature sensors
- Access to the PIC data bus for further expansion.

More importantly no in-depth knowledge of USB hardware or software is required, only an understanding of the communication protocol. The module also has the advantage of being in a 40-pin DIL pin-out, so further expansion is easy.

More information can be found at www.ftdichip.com/Documents/DataSheets/DLP/dlp-245pbv20.pdf

21.3.1 Installing the drivers

The combined driver module (CDM) D2XX drivers must be downloaded and extracted from the FTDI web site at: http://www.ftdichip.com/Drivers/D2XX.htm. This enables access through either D2XX DLL or via a COM port. The current version is 2.06.02 (March 31, 2010)

Installation instructions are available at:
http://www.dlpdesign.com/Documents/AppNotes.html (AN 104).

Having installed the drivers, you can check the device in Control Panel's Device Manager, USB Controllers. See figure 21.2.

Figure 21.2 USB Properties

The VID and PID can be seen in the details tab, figure 21.3 but we won't need to know them:

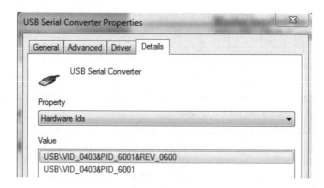

Figure 21.3 VID and PID

To see if your module works, you can try the loopback example number 3 at www.ftdichip.com/Projects/CodeExamples/CSharp.htm. Although this is for the serial version, it does detect the device and shows its properties.

This expects the FTDI drivers to be installed and you may need to add a reference to FTD2XX_NET.dll. Running it reported the following for my module:

> Device Index: 0
> Flags: 0
> Type: FT_DEVICE_232R
> ID: 4036001
> Location ID: 23
> Serial Number: DPCXXH3N
> Description: DLP-245PB

Further example software is available on purchase of the module.

21.3.2 The DLL communication software

Programs communicate with the module using the .NET class FTD2XX_NET. Download this from the FDTI web site and extract it. It needs to be added to References in Solution Explorer for every program you write. I suggest you put a copy of the DLL and XML file in the program's folder. To add the reference right-click References and Browse for the file FTD2XX_NET.DLL. This provides commands such as Read and Write so we can communicate with the module. The XML file provides information to the IntelliSense so we can see the methods and their descriptions, see figure 21.4.

Figure 21.4 IntelliSense FTD2XX_NET DLL display

There is a D2XX_Programmer's_Guide at the FDTI web site.

21.3.4 The hardware design.

There is little to do as far as the hardware is concerned. A link needs to be made from pin 20 to pin 19 if you wish to power the module from the USB bus, and obviously any connections need to be made to the inputs and outputs that you need. Figure 21.5 shows the top-view pin out and the pin descriptions are shown in Table 21.1.

Pin #	Description	Pin #	Description
1	Ground	40	Ground
2	E0 – I/O pin A/D channel 5	39	C7 – (I/O) port pin C7
3	A0 – I/O pin A/D channel 0	38	C6 – (I/O) port pin C6
4	A1 – I/O pin A/D channel 1	37	C5 – (I/O) port pin C5
5	A2 – I/O pin A/D channel 2	36	C4 – (I/O) port pin C4
6	A3 – I/O pin A/D channel 3	35	C3 – (I/O) port pin C3
7	A4 – I/O pin open drain output	34	C2 – (I/O) port pin C2
8	A5 – I/O pin A/D channel 4	33	C1 – (I/O) port pin C1
9	UPRST (in) - Reset input	32	C0 – (I/O) port pin C0
10	Ground	31	B0 – (I/O) port pin B0
11	Reset# (in) - ext. reset	30	B4 – (I/O) port pin B4
12	N/C	29	B5 – (I/O) port pin B5
13	Ground	28	DB0 – data bus 0
14	3V3OUT (out) - 3.3V output (max 5mA)	27	DB1 – data bus 1
15	Ground	26	DB2 – data bus 2
16	SWVCC (out)	25	DB3 – data bus 3
17	Ground	24	DB4 – data bus 4
18	N/C	23	DB5 – data bus 5
19	EXTVCC (in) - 5V input	22	DB6 – data bus 6
20	PORTVCC (out) - connect to pin 19 for USB powered designs	21	DB7 – data bus 7

Table 21.1 Pin descriptions

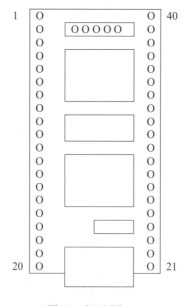

Figure 21.5 Pin out

The 5-pin connector on the device is used for programming the PIC.

In this design the module is powered by the USB interface. Connect pin 20 to pin 19 (PORTVCC (out) to EXTVCC (in)).

For the output, connect an LED and resistor to pin 2 (port E bit 0).
For the input, connect a switch and resistor to pin 32 (port C bit 0).

Once the software drivers are loaded, connect it with a USB cable. It should be recognized by Windows.

21.3.5 Communications Protocol

To communicate with the device a number of bytes is sent:

1. The number of bytes in the command and data, excluding the checksum
2. The Command
3. Data or parameters (if required)
4. CheckSum – an ExclusiveOR of the previous bytes

The device responds with a 0x55 if the checksum agrees, or 0xAA if not. This has to be read by the host PC. If you have requested data, you then read the data.

If you perform too many reads, the device will hang.

Example:
To read port D the following commands are sent:
1. 0x01   One byte command
2. 0x5B   Read port D
3. 0x5A   (0x01 EXOR 0x5B)

The response will be a 0x55 (checksum match), followed by the data from port C. Two reads of the module have to be made.

To write 0x24 to port D the following commands are sent:
1. 0x02   Two byte command
2. 0x5C   Write to port D
3. 0x24   Data
4. 0x79   (0x01 EXOR 0x5C EXOR 24)

The response will be a 0x55 (checksum match). This has to be read.

21.4 USB Module Software

Let's write a program initially to detect the device on the USB port and extend this to toggle bit 0 of port E and then reads port C. Note this code is designed for only one module only on the USB port.

Start a new project.
Add the following at the top of the code:

```
using System.Threading;
using FTD2XX_NET;
```

Add FTD2XX_NET to the References. (Right-click and browse)

We will now add all the declarations we will need. Add the following before the code public Form1( ):

```
// Create new instance of the FTDI device class
FTDI myFtdiDevice = new FTDI();
FTDI.FT_STATUS ftStatus = FTDI.FT_STATUS.FT_OK;
UInt32 numBytesWritten = 0;
UInt32 numBytesToRead = 1;
UInt32 numBytesRead=0;
byte[ ] dataBytes = new byte[5];
```

Let's see if the device is present by seeing how many there are:
Add the following to the Form load event:

```
UInt32 ftdiDevCount = 0;

// How many?
ftStatus = myFtdiDevice.GetNumberOfDevices(ref ftdiDevCount);
// Check status
if (ftStatus == FTDI.FT_STATUS.FT_OK)
  {
    MessageBox.Show("Number of FTDI devices: " +
        ftdiDevCount.ToString());
  }
else
  {
    MessageBox.Show("Failed to get number of devices: Error " +
        ftStatus.ToString());
  }

// Allocate storage for device info list
FTDI.FT_DEVICE_INFO_NODE[ ] ftdiDeviceList = new
FTDI.FT_DEVICE_INFO_NODE[ftdiDevCount];
```

```
// Populate the device list
ftStatus = myFtdiDevice.GetDeviceList(ftdiDeviceList);

// Open first device in our list by serial number – hopefully there's only one
ftStatus =
myFtdiDevice.OpenBySerialNumber(ftdiDeviceList[0].SerialNumber);
if (ftStatus != FTDI.FT_STATUS.FT_OK)
{
    MessageBox.Show("Failed to open device: Error " +
        ftStatus.ToString());
}
```

If you've added the Windows drivers, connect the module using a USB cable and run the program to see if it's working. You should get a message as shown in figure 21.6.

Number of FTDI devices: 1

OK

Figure 21.6 FTDI detect message

21.4.1 Setting outputs

Now let's extend the program to toggle output port E, bit 0 (pin 2). You can connect an LED to this pin to see the program working. To set and reset this bit the command sequence is:

1. 0x03   Three byte command
2. 0xA6   Set port pin
3. 0x48   Port pin is E0
4. 0x01   Set the bit (0 for reset)
5. 0xEC   EXOR of previous bytes – 0xED for reset

After the code: FTDI myFtdiDevice = new FTDI(); add the init code:

```
// record E0 bit state
int e0State=0;
```

Add a button to the form and for the button click code type the following:

```
// Toggle E0 pin
```

```
// To set E0 command bytes are:
// 0x03, 0xA6, 0x48, 0x01, 0xEC
// 0x03 XOR 0xA6 XOR 0x48 XOR 0x01 = 0xEC.
// and to reset E0 command is:
// 0x03, 0xA6, 0x48, 0x00, 0xED

dataBytes[0] = 0x03;    // 3 bytes (not including CS)
dataBytes[1] = 0xA6;    // set port pin
dataBytes[2] = 0x48;    // 0x48 = port E, bit 0

if (e0State==0)
{
   // then set
   e0State = 1;
   dataBytes[3] = 0x01;   // set bit
   dataBytes[4] = 0xEC;   // CS
}
else
{
   // reset
   e0State = 0;
   dataBytes[3] = 0x00;   // reset bit
   dataBytes[4] = 0xED;   // CS
}

// And write data to the device
ftStatus = myFtdiDevice.Write
       (dataBytes, dataBytes.Length, ref numBytesWritten);
if (ftStatus != FTDI.FT_STATUS.FT_OK)
{
    MessageBox.Show("Failed getting bytes: Error " + ftStatus.ToString());
}
// else OK

// read the CS message
myFtdiDevice.Read(dataBytes, numBytesToRead, ref numBytesRead);
if (dataBytes[0] == 0xAA)
{
  MessageBox.Show("Checksum error");
}
```

Try the program. The port output should switch on and off.

21.4.2 Reading Inputs

We can now try to read port C. The command sequence for this is:

1. 0x01   One byte command
2. 0x59   Read port C
3. 0x58   (0x01 EXOR 0x59)

The Write command sends a byte array or string. The checksum response is read first, followed by the data.

Add a button and the following code for the button click event:

```
// Write byte array data
dataBytes[0] = 0x01;          // one byte command
dataBytes[1] = 0x59;          // Read port C
dataBytes[2] = 0x58;          // CS = 1 xor 59

// send the command
ftStatus = myFtdiDevice.Write(dataBytes, dataBytes.Length,
        ref numBytesWritten);
if (ftStatus != FTDI.FT_STATUS.FT_OK)
{
    MessageBox.Show("Failed to write to device
        (error " + ftStatus.ToString() + ")");
}

// read response - 0xAA (170) indicates CS error, 0x55 (85) is OK
// this has to be read from the buffer.
numBytesToRead =1;
myFtdiDevice.Read(dataBytes, numBytesToRead, ref numBytesRead);
if (dataBytes[0] == 0xAA)
{
    // CS error
    MessageBox.Show("CS Error");
}
else
{
    //no CS error - read data
    numBytesToRead = 1;
    myFtdiDevice.Read(dataBytes, numBytesToRead, ref numBytesRead);
    // and display port C state
    MessageBox.Show("Port C0 = " + dataBytes[0].ToString());
}
```

The port data should be shown as in figure 21.7. Note that if the inputs are floating, their values will be indeterminant.

Figure 21.7 Port C display

Now that you know how to read and write to the ports, you can do anything. In addition though, the module has capability of connecting to analogue devices and a temperature sensor. The commands to do this are described in the manual.

You can also find out how to program the PIC to run programs for you.

21.5 Self Assessment Exercises:

1. Design a program to read and write to all the ports.

2. Write a program to read an analogue input. Either read the output set by the previous program or add a potentiometer to supply an analogue input to the module and read it.

3. The module supports commands to communicate with a Maxim DS18S20-PAR one-wire interface digital thermometer. Connect one of these to the module and write a program to read and display the temperature.

4. Write a program to generate a PWM (pulse width modulated) output signal. This can be turned into an analogue output if passed through an RC low pass filter.

5. The module contains a programmable PIC. Program this to run its own program and send data to the PC. For more information on this see the DLP design's documentation.

21.6 Summary

In this chapter we have briefly looked at the USB port. We have seen how the DLP designs DLP245PB-G module can be connected to a PC using their USB drivers. We have seen in detail how to communicate with the module and read and write to the ports, providing digital I/O and analogue input.

Chapter 22 - USB Interfacing

22.1 Introduction

The USB port has been the preferred input and output for PCs for many years now. Although a USB interface design is more complicated than using the PC's original serial or parallel ports, it is not that difficult and it is more versatile. For a simple interface the designer does not need to write drivers or understand the USB communication process (e.g. PIN, VIN and enumeration). In the case of the Microchip devices that we will consider, the hardware interface and communications software is incorporated on the target device (a PIC). Microchip also provides a USB driver and PC software in C++. In this chapter we'll see how to write a USB interface in C#.

22.2 Microchip PIC (Peripheral Interface Controller) Design

Microchip and other manufacturers provide programmable devices that interface directly to the USB port, as well as the software to deal with the USB interface at both the target (PIC) and the PC ends.

The design breaks down into the following parts:

- The PIC hardware with the USB interface
- The PIC firmware
- The PC drivers
- The PC application software

We will consider the PIC design and software in this chapter and look at the PC code and USB drivers in the next chapter.

22.3 The PIC/USB hardware

There are plenty of USB interface boards available, but these can be expensive. The PIC USB devices themselves are inexpensive and we shall study the design of an interface board. The design is simple and can even be made on strip board.

Microchip manufactures many PIC devices with USB interfaces. One of the most commonly used is the PIC18F2455/2550/4455/4550 family. We will not look at the PIC devices in detail here as there are plenty of books on PIC design.

The PIC18F2xxx are 28 pin devices and the PIC18F4xxx are 40 pin devices and consequently have more I/O pins. The PIC18Fx550 has slightly more program memory. In this design we will use the PIC18F4550-I/P 40 pin DIL device.

Table 22.1 shows the main PIC features; in addition they have timers, capture compare registers etc. For more information, see the Microchip web site, www.microchip.com.

Features \ PIC	PIC18F2455	PIC18F2550	PIC18F4455	PIC18F4550
Operating Frequency	DC – 48 MHz	DC – 48 MHz	DC – 48 MHz	DC – 48 MHz
Program Memory (Bytes)	24576	32768	24576	32768
Data Memory (Bytes)	2048	2048	2048	2048
Data EEPROM Memory (Bytes)	256	256	256	256
I/O Ports	A, B, C, (E)	A, B, C, (E)	A, B, C, D, E	A, B, C, D, E

Table 22.1: PIC device features

22.4 The USB PIC Hardware interface

The hardware design provides two switches for input, four LEDs for PIC status and output and a potentiometer to demonstrate analogue input. The design is simple: the PIC18F4550 interfaces directly to the USB port and only a crystal and a few capacitors are needed to get the PIC running. No power supply is needed – it is taken from the USB port.

Figure 22.1 PIC18F4550 USB circuit diagram

The two switches are on port B bits 0 and 1. The four LEDs are on port D bits 0 to 3. The potentiometer is connected to analogue input AN0 on port A. The power is taken from the USB port. The USB connector is a B-type. The circuit diagram is shown in figure 22.1.

The board layout is quite compact and shown in figure 22.2.

Figure 22.2 PCB layout

You can of course use Microchip's own PICDEM board as your hardware, see: http://ww1.microchip.com/downloads/en/devicedoc/51526a.pdf

22.5 The PIC firmware

22.5.1 Introduction

Microchip provides a free integrated development environment called MPLAB that compiles and debugs code for their PICs. They also provide a free C compiler (MCC18) that is used by MPLAB. We won't be covering these products in detail here; more details are available from the MPLAB® IDE link on the Microchip web site.

For the PIC firmware, we will use Microchip's software called MCHPFSUSB (Microchip full-speed USB framework). This is best found by searching Microchip's web site for 'PICDEM Full Speed USB demo board'.

The Microchip USB Device Framework provides the necessary software to interface to the USB port. The detail design is in their publication Microchip USB Device Firmware Framework User's Guide, DS51679B.

The Framework provides a set of interfaces that handle the USB communications. The main code is an infinite while loop that calls the USB tasks (in USBTasks( )) and the user's code. USBTasks( ) polls and services the USB hardware interrupts. The user's code is added in the function ProcessIO in user.c. The user code can call the functions USBGenWrite and USBGenRead to send or receive a USB data packet if necessary.

When downloaded the software extracts to its own folder called 'Microchip Solutions'. Many examples are included in the download. The files we will use are in the 'USB Device - MCHPUSB - Generic Driver Demo' folder and this includes the PIC USB firmware (which we will modify), the PC software (in C++ - we will write our own) and DLL library (mpusbapi.dll). The Windows USB driver (mchpusb.sys or mchpusb.sys for 64-bit systems) is also here and asked for when the hardware is attached.

We will download, modify and program the PIC with the PIC USB firmware. It is found in the sub-folder: 'Generic Driver Demo – Firmware'. Should you need it, further information is in the 'Getting Started - Running the Device - MCHPUSB - Generic driver demo.html' documentation in this folder.

This firmware doesn't read the switches. To demonstrate how the firmware is modified and to get some idea of how messages are sent between the PC and PIC, we will add a command to do this. We will cover the steps briefly here, but it helps if you know how to use Microchip's MPLAB. You will also need a PIC programmer, an excellent design is at: http://usbpicprog.org.

22.5.2 Modifying the firmware

Start MPLAB and open the 'USB Device - MCHPUSB - Generic Driver - C18 - PICDEM FSUSB.mcw' workspace found in the 'Generic Driver Demo – Firmware' folder.

22.5.3 The protocol

The user.c file contains the user's code and the commands are placed in the function called ServiceRequests. The data that is sent to the PIC is an array called OUTPacket. It is in the form of a command followed by data. The responses to the PC are placed in an array called INPacket. This is sent to the PC by the Microchip firmware.

The firmware reads the OUTPacket array and executes a switch on the command received from the USB port (the first byte: OUTPacket.CMD); we will add another case statement (to read our switches) to this.

Commands to update the LEDs and read the potentiometer are already included:

```
UPDATE_LED = 0x32;
RD_POT = 0x37;
```

Also included are READ_VERSION, ID_BOARD and RESET commands (0x00, 0x31, 0xFF respectively). There are also some other commands that can't be used because the hardware isn't implemented in this design.

The UPDATE_LED command shows how the command's data is read from OUTPacket, for example:

```
if(OUTPacket.led_num == 3)              // LED 3?
    {
        if(OUTPacket.led_status)         // led_status true ?
        {
            mLED_3_On();                 // switch it on
        }
```

The READ_VERSION code shows how data is returned to the PC using the INPacket array:

```
case READ_VERSION:
    //dataPacket._byte[1] is command length
    INPacket._byte[2] = MINOR_VERSION;
    INPacket._byte[3] = MAJOR_VERSION;
    counter=0x04;     // send 4 bytes: cmd, length, minor and major version
```

As you can see the program fills the array with the required data. It is then sent to the PC by the Microchip firmware.

22.5.4 Adding commands to the firmware

To add your own commands you define a value for your command and add it to the switch statement. Let's add a command to read the switches; we shall use the value 0x40.

Add the enumerated command to set the switches to the code in the user.h file. Change the code so that it reads:

```
RD_POT          = 0x37;
READ_SWITCH     = 0x40;       // read switches on port B
RESET           = 0xFF;
```

Change the code in the initialization section of user.c to the following so that RB0 and RB1 are set as PIC inputs:

```
void UserInit(void)
{
    mInitAllLEDs();
    mInitAllSwitches();
    TRISBbits.TRISB0=1; TRISBbits.TRISB1=1;
```

Finally add the code to read the switches and send the data back via the USB port to the PC application. Change the user.c code to add the case for READ_SWITCH:

```
switch(OUTPacket.CMD)
{
    case READ_SWITCH:
        counter = 0x02;      // reply with 2 bytes: command and status
        // which switch?
        if(OUTPacket.ID == 0)
        {
            // it's switch 0 on RB0 - return value in second byte
            if(PORTBbits.RB0) INPacket._byte[1]=1;
            else INPacket._byte[1]=0;
        }
        else if(OUTPacket.ID == 1)
        {
            // it's swich 1 on RB1
            if(PORTBbits.RB1) INPacket._byte[1]=1;
            else INPacket._byte[1]=0;
        }
        else
            // no switch defined make 255 error message
            INPacket._byte[1]=255;
        break;

    (case READ_VERSION: code then follows)
```

To compile the firmware choose Project > Build All. This creates a hex file called USB Device - MCHPUSB - Generic Driver - C18 - PICDEM FSUSB.hex which can be programmed into the PIC.

22.6 The USB drivers

The hardware can now be connected to the PC, which should recognize it and ask for the USB driver. This is called mchpusb.sys and is in the 'Driver and inf' sub-folder of

'USB Device - MCHPUSB – Generic Driver Demo'. Install the drivers as usual for USB hardware.

22.7 Summary

We have studied some of the Microchip PIC devices that support the USB interface and seen how easy it is to interface the hardware to the PC USB port. We have used the Microchip design tools (IDE and MCC18 C compiler) to modify Microchip provided software to add new functions on the PIC. This has been compiled and the PIC programmed. On connecting to the PC, the hardware is recognized and the drivers loaded.

In the next chapter we will turn to the PC program.

Chapter 23 - USB interfacing - The PC code

23.1 Introduction

In this chapter we will look at the Microchip DLLs that interface to the USB port. These are used in a C# application that sends commands to the PIC hardware designed in the previous chapter and displayed the responses on a user interface.

We will see how to solve the problems when running this under Windows 7.

23.2 The Microchip MPUSBAPI DLL libraries

Microchip provides DLL code to interface the PC code with the USB. These are Win API functions used to interface to the USB port at the PC. The basic calls we will use are:

- MPUSBOpen – Opens a link (a pipe) to the USB device with a matching PID and VID and returns a handle that is used by the read and write commands.
- MPUSBClose - closes a given handle
- MPUSBRead – reads data from a specific handle
- MPUSBWrite – writes data to a specific handle

More information is provided in the Microchip solutions folder: usbTools/mchpusb custom driver/mpusbapi and in the C++ code: /DLL/Borland_C/Source/_mpusbapi.cpp

Microchip provides examples of using these DLLs in Delphi and C++. The declarations in C# are:

```
[DllImport("mpusbapi.dll")]
private static extern UInt32 _MPUSBGetDLLVersion();

[DllImport("mpusbapi.dll")]
private static extern UInt32 _MPUSBGetDeviceCount(string pVID_PID);

[DllImport("mpusbapi.dll")]
private static extern IntPtr _MPUSBOpen(UInt32 instance,
        string pVID_PID, string pEP, UInt32 dwDir, UInt32 dwReserved);

[DllImport("mpusbapi.dll")]
private static extern bool _MPUSBClose(IntPtr handle);

[DllImport("mpusbapi.dll")]
private static extern UInt32 _MPUSBRead(IntPtr handle, byte[] pData,
        UInt32 dwLen, ref UInt32 pLength, UInt32 dwMilliseconds);

[DllImport("mpusbapi.dll")]
```

```
        private static extern UInt32 _MPUSBWrite(IntPtr handle, byte[] pData,
                UInt32 dwLen, ref UInt32 pLength, UInt32 dwMilliseconds);

    [DllImport("mpusbapi.dll")]
    private static extern UInt32 _MPUSBReadInt(IntPtr handle, byte[] pData,
                UInt32 dwLen, ref UInt32 pLength, UInt32 dwMilliseconds);
```

Example code for the use of these calls follow:

1. _MPUSBOpen

```
    UInt32 selection = 0;        // selects USB device – only one assumed here
    string vid_pid = "vid_04d8&pid_000c";   // vid and pid of USB device
    string out_pipe = "\\MCHP_EP1";
    IntPtr myOutPipe = _MPUSBOpen(selection, vid_pid, out_pipe, 0, 0);
```

2. _MPUSBWrite

```
    byte[] sendData;             // 64 byte array containging data
    uint sendLength;     // number of bytes in message
    UInt32 sentDataLength = 0;        // actual number of bytes sent
    UInt32 sendDelay = 1000; // milliseconds
    _MPUSBWrite(myOutPipe, sendData, sendLength, ref sentDataLength,
    sendDelay)
```

3. _MPUSBRead

```
    byte[] receiveData;          // array containing data received from PIC
    UInt32 expectedReceiveLength;  // number of bytes expected back
    UInt32 receiveLength;        // bytes received - altered by method ('ref')
    UInt32 receiveDelay = 1000;        // milliseconds
    _MPUSBRead(myInPipe, receiveData, expectedReceiveLength,
            ref receiveLength, receiveDelay)
                // can check that receiveLength== expectedReceiveLength
```

4. _MPUSBClose

```
    _MPUSBClose(myOutPipe);
```

We'll use these in the next section.

23.2.1 Windows 7 exceptions

These calls work well with VS2010 and XP, but with Windows 7 a
PinvokeStackImbalance or a BadImageFormatException exception occurs when the DLL

loads. The solution is to change the Active Solution Platform to x86, see figure 23.1. I can only do this with the Professional Edition however.

The procedure is to right-click Solution <program name> in Solution explorer - You can also use Alt-Enter.
This displays 'property pages' – click the Configuration Properties tab.
Click Configuration Manager to display the Configuration Manager window.
Select Active Solution platform - and select x86. You may have to click New and type in x86. Click Close and OK
Now put the mpusbapi.dll in the new folder x86 > Bin > Debug

Figure 23.1 Changing the Active solution platform

23.3 The C# application

In this application will design a user interface that has commands to set or reset the LEDs, read the switches and read the analogue input. It will include a class that has the USB read and USB write commands.

On selecting a command, a string containing the command and data is sent to the PIC, which executes the command and returns any data if needed.

The steps to create the application are as follows

1. Create a new project and the user interface with buttons that read the state of the switches and the analogue input value and set the state of the LEDs.
2. Add the USB interface class code
3. Add the code for the buttons.

1. Create new project and interface

Start a new project (I've called it USBPICInterface). To the form add two buttons to read the switch states, two buttons to change the LEDs (the background colour of these will display their state -gray for off and red for on), a button to read the analogue input and a ProgressBar with a label to display the analogue voltage (set its range to 0-1023).

It should be similar to figure 23.2

Figure 23.2 The USB User Interface

2. Add the USB Interface class code.

Select Project > Add Class and call it USBInterface.

At the top of the code add the command:

```
using System.Runtime.InteropServices;
```

Enter the following code for the USBInterface class. This is quite a long piece of code.

```
namespace USBPICDesignInterface
{
  class USBInterface
  {
   [DllImport("mpusbapi.dll")]
   private static extern UInt32 _MPUSBGetDLLVersion();
   [DllImport("mpusbapi.dll")]
   private static extern UInt32 _MPUSBGetDeviceCount(string pVID_PID);
   [DllImport("mpusbapi.dll")]
   private static extern IntPtr _MPUSBOpen(UInt32 instance, string pVID_PID,
        string pEP, UInt32 dwDir, UInt32 dwReserved);
   [DllImport("mpusbapi.dll")]
   private static extern bool _MPUSBClose(IntPtr handle);
   [DllImport("mpusbapi.dll")]
   private static extern UInt32 _MPUSBRead(IntPtr handle, byte[] pData,
```

```csharp
        UInt32 dwLen, ref UInt32 pLength, UInt32 dwMilliseconds);
[DllImport("mpusbapi.dll")]
private static extern UInt32 _MPUSBWrite(IntPtr handle, byte[] pData,
        UInt32 dwLen, ref UInt32 pLength, UInt32 dwMilliseconds);
[DllImport("mpusbapi.dll")]
private static extern UInt32 _MPUSBReadInt(IntPtr handle, byte[] pData,
        UInt32 dwLen, ref UInt32 pLength, UInt32 dwMilliseconds);

string vid_pid = "vid_04d8&pid_000c";

// Define End Points
string out_pipe = "\\MCHP_EP1";
string in_pipe = "\\MCHP_EP1";

IntPtr myOutPipe;
IntPtr myInPipe;

private void OpenPipes()
{
  UInt32 selection = 0; // Selects the device to connect to
                // Only one is assumed here.

  myOutPipe = _MPUSBOpen(selection, vid_pid, out_pipe, 0, 0);
  myInPipe = _MPUSBOpen(selection, vid_pid, in_pipe, 1, 0);

            // dwDir: write = 0, read =1
}

private void ClosePipes()
{
  _MPUSBClose(myOutPipe);
  _MPUSBClose(myInPipe);
}

private UInt32 SendReceivePacket(byte[] sendData, uint sendLength,
            byte[] receiveData, ref UInt32 receiveLength)
{
  // SendReceivePacket - from console.cpp
  // Pass:
  // SendData (txBuffer) is a byte array containing the message
  // sendLength is number of bytes to send
  // rxData is byte array containing data sent back
  // rxLength contains the number of bytes received
  // (returned by the PIC, hence 'ref')
  //
  // Returns 1 if successful, 2, if partial comms (unexpected length returned)
```

```
    // 0 if fail

    UInt32 sendDelay = 1000;
    UInt32 receiveDelay = 1000;

    UInt32 sentDataLength = 0;
    UInt32 expectedReceiveLength = receiveLength;

    OpenPipes();

    if (_MPUSBWrite(myOutPipe, sendData, sendLength, ref sentDataLength,
        sendDelay)==1)
    {
      if (_MPUSBRead(myInPipe, receiveData, expectedReceiveLength,
              ref receiveLength, receiveDelay)==1)
      {
        if (receiveLength == expectedReceiveLength)
        {
          ClosePipes();
          return 1;  // Success!
        }
        else if (receiveLength < expectedReceiveLength)
        {
          ClosePipes();
          return 2;  // Partially failed, incorrect receive length
        } //end if else
      } // end if (_MPUSBRead
    } // end if (_MPUSBWrite

    // write failed
    ClosePipes();
    return 0;  // Operation Failed
  } //end of SendReceivePacket

  public UInt32 GetDLLVersion()
  {
    return _MPUSBGetDLLVersion();
  }

  public UInt32 GetDeviceCount(string Vid_Pid)
  {
    return _MPUSBGetDeviceCount(Vid_Pid);
  }

  public int ReadSwitch(byte SwitchNumber)
  {
```

```
// ReadSwitch method - Reads state of switch
// Pass: switch to read (0 on RB0 and 1 on RB1)
// Returns: 0 or 1, or -1 if error
// Example call: int switchState = ReadSwitch(0);
// (then check for error, i.e, switchState = -1)
//
// sends command (0x40) to PIC, followed by switch number
// e.g. 0x40,0x00 would read switch 0
//
// rxbuffer set to 64 bytes (equal or larger than max endpoint size)

const byte RDSWITCHCMD = 0x40;  // ReadSwitch command
byte[] txBuffer = new byte[64];
byte[] rxBuffer = new byte[64];

uint txLength = 2;

// send 2 bytes of data, expect 2 bytes (command and state)
// if 1 is returned, communication was successful
// if 2 comms failed
txBuffer[0] = RDSWITCHCMD;
txBuffer[1] = SwitchNumber;

UInt32 rxLength = 2;      // receives command (0x40), state (true/false)

if (SendReceivePacket(txBuffer, txLength, rxBuffer, ref rxLength) == 1)
{
   return (int)rxBuffer[1];   // It's OK
}
else
{
   return -1;  // error
}
}

public int UpdateLED(byte led, bool state)
{
  // UpdateLED method - sets or resets LED
  // Calls PIC UPDATE_LED command, which only updates LED 3 or 4
  // Pass: LED to change (3 on RD2, 4 on RD3), and true or false (on or off)
  // Returns: 1 if OK, -1 if error
  // Example call: int ledStatus = UpdateLED(3,true); // set LED 3
  // (then check for error, i.e, ledStatus = -1)
  //
  // sends PIC UPDATE_LED command (0x32) to PIC,
  // followed by the LED to update, and 0 or 1
```

```
// e.g. <0x32><0x03><0x01>  to turn on LED 3
//
// rxbuffer set to 64 bytes (equal or larger than max endpoint size)

byte[] txBuffer = new byte[64];
byte[] rxBuffer = new byte[64];

const byte UPDATE_LED = 0x32;

uint txLength = 3;

txBuffer[0] = UPDATE_LED;
txBuffer[1] = led;
if (state) txBuffer[2] = 1;
else txBuffer[2] = 0;

UInt32 rxLength = 1;  //only command returned

// send 3 bytes of data, if 1 is returned, communication was successful
// if 2 comms failed

if (SendReceivePacket(txBuffer, txLength, rxBuffer, ref rxLength) == 1)
{
  return 0;
}
else
{
  return -1;
}
}

public int ReadPot()
{
  // ReadPot method - Reads analog input on AN0
  // Pass: nothing
  // returns -1 if error else 1- bit adc value

  // PIC RD_POT returns 3 bytes: cmd, addresslow(byte[1]), addresshigh(byte[0])
  // the 10-bit right justified POT value
  //
  // Example call: uint potValue = ReadPot();
  //
  // sends command (READPOT = 0x37) to PIC
  //
  // rxbuffer must be equal or larger than max endpoint size, set to 64 bytes.

  const byte READPOTCMD = 0x37;  // ReadPot command
```

```
byte[] txBuffer = new byte[64];
byte[] rxBuffer = new byte[64];

uint txLength = 1;

// send 1 bytes of data, expect 3 bytes (command and 2 bytes )
// if 1 is returned, communication was successful
txBuffer[0] = READPOTCMD;

UInt32 rxLength = 3;      // receives command (0x37), bytes

if (SendReceivePacket(txBuffer, txLength, rxBuffer, ref rxLength) == 1)
{
  // It's OK
  int result = rxBuffer[2];
  result = (((rxBuffer[2])<<8)| rxBuffer[1]);
  return result;
}
else
{
  return -1;  // error
}

}
}
}
```

More information on this code can be found by looking at the console.cpp code in the Microchip folder.

Now we can add our commands to read the switches and analogue input and change the LEDs

3. Add the code for the buttons

Change the form.cs code at the top of the form to instantiate a new USBInterface class as follows:

```
public partial class USBForm : Form
  {
    USBInterface MyUSBInterface = new USBInterface();
```

Change the code for the button click events to the following:

```
private void btnRdSw1_Click(object sender, EventArgs e)
{
  // read switch
```

```
        int swStatus = MyUSBInterface.ReadSwitch(0);   // no error check
        if (swStatus != -1)
        {
           if (swStatus == 0)
           {
              btnRdSw1.Text = "Sw1 is off";
           }
           if (swStatus == 1)
           {
              btnRdSw1.Text = "Sw1 is on";
           }
        }
     }

private void btnRdSw2_Click(object sender, EventArgs e)
     {
        // read switch
        int swStatus = MyUSBInterface.ReadSwitch(1);   // no error check
        if (swStatus == 0)
        {
           btnRdSw2.Text = "Sw2 off";
        }
        if (swStatus == 1)
        {
           btnRdSw2.Text = "Sw2 on";
        }
     }
```

Change the code for the LED buttons to the following:

```
     private void btnChangeLED3_Click(object sender, EventArgs e)
     {
        if (btnChangeLED3.Text == "Set LED 3")
        {
           // send set led command
           MyUSBInterface.UpdateLED(3, true); // set led 3, ignore response?
           btnChangeLED3.Text = "Reset LED 3";   // change text
           btnChangeLED3.BackColor = Color.Red;   // update color
        }
        else
        {
           // send reset led command
           MyUSBInterface.UpdateLED(3, false);
           btnChangeLED3.Text = "Set LED 3";
           btnChangeLED3.BackColor = Color.LightGray;
        }
```

```
        }

        private void btnChangeLED4_Click(object sender, EventArgs e)
        {
            if (btnChangeLED4.Text == "Set LED 4")
            {
                // send set led command
                MyUSBInterface.UpdateLED(4, true);  // set led 4, ignore response?
                btnChangeLED4.Text = "Reset LED 4";   // change text
                btnChangeLED4.BackColor = Color.Red;   // update color
            }
            else
            {
                // send reset led command
                MyUSBInterface.UpdateLED(4, false);
                btnChangeLED4.Text = "Set LED 4";
                btnChangeLED4.BackColor = Color.LightGray;
            }

        }
```

Finally change the code for the button that reads the analogue input to the following:

```
        private void btnRdAtoD_Click(object sender, EventArgs e)
        {
            // send command to read a to d on port AN0
            // PIC command RD_POT = 0x37
            // returns int, -1 if error, 10 bit value of ADC otherwise
            int ADCResult = MyUSBInterface.ReadPot();
            if (ADCResult != -1)
            {
                // no error
                pbarAtoD.Value = ADCResult; // result is 10 bits 0 -1023
                //pbar range 0-1023, so no conversion needed
                lblVolts.Text = "Analogue voltage is: " +
                    (ADCResult * 5.0 / 1023).ToString("#0.00");
            }
        }
```

Copy the mpusbapi.dll file into the Debug folder. Compile and run the the code. The program should work and commands sent from the PC should be executed and responses set back to the PC.

To save you typing all this, the full code is available from Elektor's web site.

23.4 Self Assessment exercises

I'm sure if you've got this far, you can think of many exercises for yourself, but you might like to look at the PIC USB bootloader and C# article at:
http://eegeek.net/content/view/27/32/1/1/

23.5 Summary

In this chapter we have seen the Microchip DLLs that interface to the USB port. In particular the Open, Write, Read and Close methods. The problems in using these with Window 7 have been solved. A C# application has been developed that sends commands and data to the PIC hardware designed in the previous chapter and the responses displayed on a user interface.

Chapter 24 - Conclusion

The idea behind this book was to enable you to understand the .NET environment and programming in C#, ultimately to interface your hardware to a PC and provide a useful user interface for your designs.

In doing so it has covered a lot of ground; from the software aspects of the .NET framework and libraries, the C# programming language; file handling; threading and internet communication, through to graphical interfacing and database handling. It moved on to hardware interfacing using the serial port control, using an external DLL to drive the parallel port and the USB port, finally producing a complete USB design.

I hope that the book has provided enough to get you going, that the examples have been clear and that it has spurred you on to your own designs.

Of course there is still a lot more you can learn, from using Windows Presentation Foundation (WPF); more detailed Object Oriented Programming such as polymorphism and delegates; advanced relational databases and searching with LINQ; to XML, cloud computing and Web Services, as well as more detailed hardware USB interfacing.

I hope that this book has given you the background and confidence to discover these for yourself. I wish you all the best in your designs.

Index